Volume Two

Sadlier Math

Catherine D. LeTourneau

Allan E. Bellman, Ph.D.

Jill A. Perry, Ph.D.

 Sadlier School

The Publisher of *Progress in Mathematics*

Program Reviewers

The publisher wishes to thank for their comments and suggestions the following teachers and administrators, who read portions of the series prior to publication.

Marcia J. Phillips
Curriculum Director/Assistant Principal
Happy Valley School-Peoria
Peoria, Arizona

Elizabeth Snow
Principal
Sacred Heart Cathedral School
Pensacola, Florida

Jodie L. Dawe
Teacher, Grade 3
Christopher Elementary School
Christopher, Illinois

Lynn M. LeTourneau
Principal
Our Lady of Charity
Cicero, Illinois

Jane Carrillo
Teacher, Kindergarten
St. Leo School
Versailles, Kentucky

Judy Helton
Teacher, Grade 2
St. Leo School
Versailles, Kentucky

Esther Park
Teacher, Grade 4
Saint Columbkille Partnership School
Brighton, Massachusetts

Molly Schwaiger
Academic Director
Partnership Academy
Richfield, Minnesota

Dr. Jeanne Gearon
Principal
Our Lady of Lourdes Catholic School
Saint Louis, Missouri

Lisa A. Nelson, Ph.D.
Assistant Principal
St. Vincent de Paul School
Omaha, Nebraska

Barbara Jones
Mathematics Department Chair
Rumson Country Day School
Rumson, New Jersey

Theresa Hurst
Teacher, Grade 2
St. Martin de Porres Marianist School
Uniondale, New York

Kimberly N. Stevenson
Principal
Holy Trinity Catholic School
McKees Rocks, Pennsylvania

Chad Riley, Ph.D.
Principal
St. Joseph Catholic School
Arlington, Texas

Cover Series Design: Silver Linings Studios

Photo Credits

Cover: Alamy Stock Photo/age fotostock: *bottom*; iStockphoto.com/ThomasTakacs: *top*.

Interior: age fotostock/View Stock: 381, 382. Alamy Stock Photo/Pablo Scapinachis Armstrong: 339, 340; inga spence: 583, 584; Panther Media GmbH/Simons: 427, 428. Dreamstime.com/Olga Kostenko: 298 *background*, 340 *background*, 382 *background*, 428 *background*, 458 *background*, 496 *background*, 554 *background*, 584 *background*. Fotolia.com/aberenyi: 495, 496. Getty Images/Jeff Hunter: 457, 458. Shutterstock.com/cdrin: 553, 554; milosk50: 297, 298. United States coin images from the United States Mint.

Ilustrators

Bob Holt, Scott Borroughs, Sarah Beise, Nathan Jarvis, Jose Ramos, Joseph Taylor. Shutterstock.com/Agor2012, incredible_movements, miniaria, whanwhan.ai, Zmiter.

is a registered trademark of William H. Sadlier, Inc.

Printed in the United States of America.
ISBN: 978-1-4217-8992-7
5 6 7 8 9 10 11 12 SHNW 26 25 24 23 22

For additional online resources, go to SadlierConnect.com.

Welcome to Sadlier Math

Dear Second Grader,

Do you know why math is important? Well, we all use math every day. We use it when we:

- measure an object
- read a map
- shop
- solve a puzzle
- build something
- and much more!

Throughout this book are special signs and symbols. When you see them, be sure to stop and look.

Objective This is what you will be studying in the lesson.

Math Words Look at these words. They are important words for the lesson.

Problem Solving Get ready to apply math in real-world contexts.

Write About It This is a question or topic for you to write about.

PRACTICE These are exercises for you to show what you know.

MORE PRACTICE These are exercises for you to build more understanding.

HOMEWORK These are exercises for you to do at home.

We wrote this book just for you!

The Authors

Hi. We are your new math friends. When you see us, pay attention. We have a lot to say!

CONTENTS

Chapter 1 Addition Within 20

Chapter 2 Subtraction Within 20

Chapter 3 Place Value to 100

The upper half of your book's front cover shows a reconstructed log cabin in Valley Forge, Pennsylvania. Cabins like this were used by soldiers during the Revolutionary War, almost 250 years ago.

Chapter 4 Addition: Two-Digit Numbers

Chapter 5 Subtraction: Two-Digit Numbers

Chapter 6 Measurement

Chapter 7 Place Value to 1000

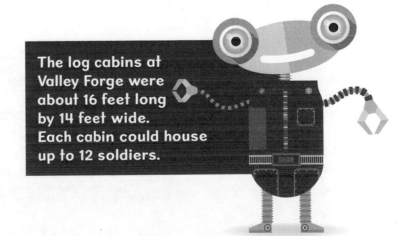

The log cabins at Valley Forge were about 16 feet long by 14 feet wide. Each cabin could house up to 12 soldiers.

Chapter 8 Addition: Three-Digit Numbers

The lower half of the front cover shows the Hemisfèric (in the foreground) and the Palau de les Arts (in the background). These buildings are part of the City of Arts and Sciences in Valencia, Spain.

Chapter 9 Subtraction: Three-Digit Numbers

Chapter 10 Foundations for Multiplication

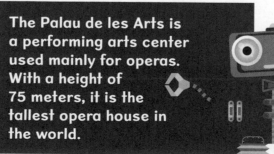

The Palau de les Arts is a performing arts center used mainly for operas. With a height of 75 meters, it is the tallest opera house in the world.

Chapter 11 Data and Graphical Displays

Chapter 12 Money and Time

Chapter 13 Geometry

The Hemisfèric, also known as the "eye of knowledge," was built to resemble a giant eye. Inside is a huge planetarium shaped like half of a sphere.

Chapter 14 Equal Shares

Place Value to 1000

A dam is a structure that is built to hold back water. Some dams are made by people, but beavers build dams too.

By the Numbers

◆ The Hoover Dam is about 726 feet tall.

◆ It is made up of about 215 blocks of concrete.

◆ It took about 5 years to build the Hoover Dam.

How Does a Dam Change the Land?

◆ The Hoover Dam was built on the Colorado River. Lake Mead formed behind the dam. It is the largest man-made lake in the United States!

◆ What are some other man-made lakes?

Dear Family,

In this chapter, we will be learning about place value to 1000.

Here are the key Math Words for this chapter:

hundred flat	**tens**
expanded form	**ones**
hundreds	**compare**

Terms such as *ones* and *tens* are not new to students. Some Math Words are repeated, as they set a foundation for building students' understanding of place value and fluency with numbers.

Use the glossary to find the definition of each word and help your child make flash cards to study throughout the chapter.

During this chapter about place value to 1000, we also will be making STEAM (Science, Technology, Engineering, the Arts, and Mathematics) connections about dam designs and engineering. Read the opening to the chapter together.

Keep Your Skills Sharp

Here is a **Keep Your Skills Sharp** activity to do at home to prepare for this chapter.

Play number riddles with your child. One player thinks of a two-digit number and gives clues to the other player. For example, "My number has a tens digit with a value of 90. The ones digit is 1 less than the tens digit. What is my number?" (98) Take turns giving and receiving clues.

Name _____

Hundreds

Objectives
- Recognize 10 tens as 1 hundred.
- Recognize place value of numbers to 900.

Math Words
hundred flat
hundred

Paige has 20 boxes of pencils.
Each box has 10 pencils in it.
How many pencils does Paige have?

Use 20 ten rods to show the 20 boxes.
Group 10 ten rods to make a hundred flat.
A hundred flat represents 1 hundred, or 100 ones.

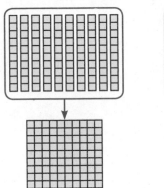
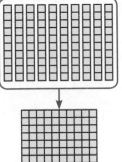

hundreds	tens	ones
2	0	0

10 tens = 1 hundred or 100   20 tens = 2 hundreds or 200

▷ Paige has 200 pencils.

PRACTICE

Circle groups of 100. Write how many tens and hundreds.

1.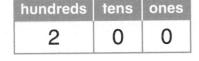

hundreds	tens	ones

_____ tens = _____ hundreds

Write the number.

2. 8 hundreds 0 tens 0 ones

____ hundreds = _____

3. 2 hundreds 0 tens 0 ones

____ hundreds = _____

4. 400 = ____ tens

5. 800 = ____ tens

6. 60 tens = ____ hundreds

7. 90 tens = ____ hundreds

Problem Solving

8. Emily has 5 bags of coins. There are 100 coins in each bag. How many coins does Emily have?

Emily has _____ coins.

9. A school library has 400 new books to put on shelves. Each shelf holds 10 books. How many shelves are needed to hold the new books? Explain.

_____ shelves are needed.

_____

_____

Write About It

10. What are three different ways you can name the number 900? Explain your thinking.

_____

_____

_____

Hundreds

You can show the same number using different place-value models.

How many hundreds are in 20 tens?

Group 10 ten rods to make one hundred flat. A hundred flat represents 1 hundred. 1 hundred is the same as 100 ones.

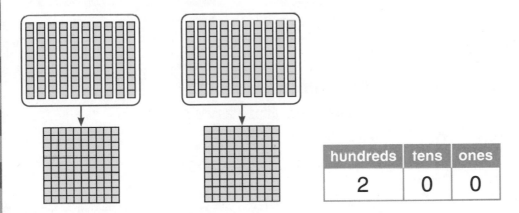

hundreds	tens	ones
2	0	0

➤ 20 ten rods are the same as 2 hundred flats.

MORE PRACTICE

Circle groups of 100. Write how many tens and hundreds.

1.

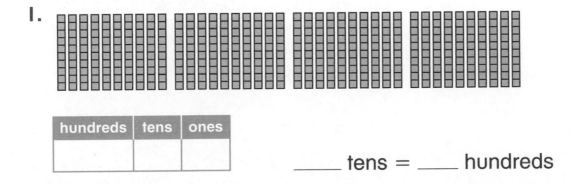

hundreds	tens	ones

_____ tens = _____ hundreds

Write the number.

1. 7 hundreds 0 tens 0 ones

   ____ hundreds = _____

2. 3 hundreds 0 tens 0 ones

   ____ hundreds = _____

3. 900 = ____ tens

4. 600 = ____ tens

5. 20 tens = ____ hundreds

6. 70 tens = ____ hundreds

Problem Solving

7. Tyler has 600 baseball cards. He puts 100 cards in each album. How many albums does Tyler fill with baseball cards?

   Tyler fills ____ albums.

8. There are 50 cases of juice boxes at a school picnic. There are 10 juice boxes in each case. How many juice boxes are at the picnic?

   _____ juice boxes

Write About It

9. A warehouse packs 800 copies of the same book into boxes. There are 10 books in each box. Lydia thinks there are 8 boxes filled with the books. Is she correct? Explain why or why not.

   _____

   _____

   _____

Hundreds, Tens, and Ones

Objective
■ Use numerals and number names to read and write numbers to 1000.

Math Word
three-digit number

A store has 2 boxes of 100 pens,
36 boxes of 10 pens, and 4 individual pens.
What number tells how many pens in all?

Use models to show the pens.
Group tens to make hundreds.

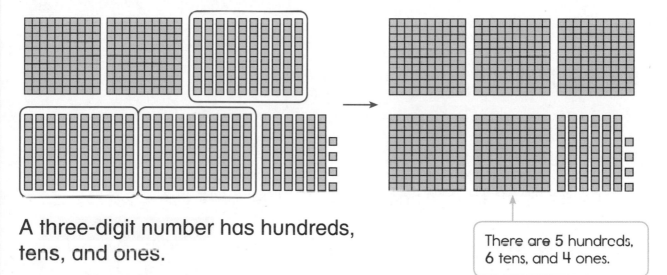

There are 5 hundreds, 6 tens, and 4 ones.

A three-digit number has hundreds, tens, and ones.

hundreds	tens	ones
5	6	4

five hundred sixty-four

➤ The number 564 tells how many pens in all.

PRACTICE

Group tens to make hundreds. Write the number and the number name.

1.

hundreds	tens	ones

_____ hundred _____

Write the number and the number name.
Group tens to make hundreds if needed.

2. 8 hundreds 5 tens 6 ones

_____   _____

3. I hundred 28 tens 7 ones

_____   _____

Match the description with the number.

4. 6 hundreds 19 tens 8 ones   707

5. 7 hundreds 0 tens 7 ones   787

6. 5 hundreds 28 tens 7 ones   798

Problem Solving

7. A school store has I box of 100 rulers, 35 boxes of 10 rulers, and 2 individual rulers.
How many rulers are in the school store?

There are _____ rulers in the school store.

Write About It

8. Nathan and Justin each used base ten blocks to show 503. Nathan used 5 hundred flats and 3 ten rods. Justin used 4 hundred flats, 10 ten rods and 3 ones cubes. Who is correct? Explain.

_____

_____

_____

Name _____

Hundreds, Tens, and Ones

A model shows 2 hundreds, 36 tens, and 4 ones. What number tells how many in all?

Group tens to make hundreds.

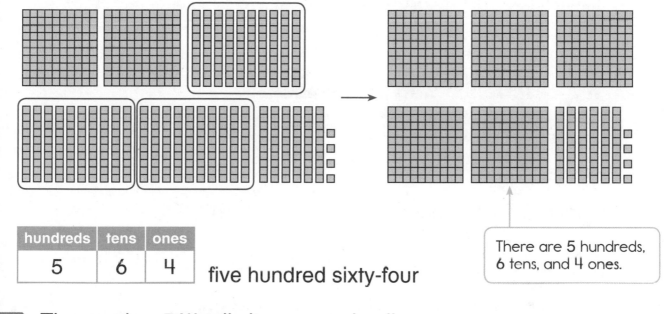

hundreds	tens	ones
5	6	4

five hundred sixty-four

There are 5 hundreds, 6 tens, and 4 ones.

The number 564 tells how many in all.

MORE PRACTICE

Group tens to make hundreds. Write the number and the number name.

1.

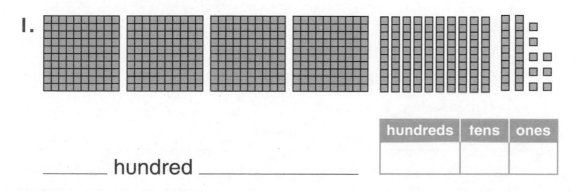

_____ hundred _____

hundreds	tens	ones

Write the number and the number name.
Group tens to make hundreds if needed.

1. 5 hundreds 4 tens 8 ones

   _____   _____

2. 3 hundreds 34 tens 2 ones

   _____   _____

Match the description with the number.

3. 0 hundreds 11 tens 0 ones   150

4. 1 hundred 5 tens 0 ones   215

5. 2 hundreds 1 ten 5 ones   110

Problem Solving

6. Carter has 28 sheets of paper. He buys 6 boxes
   that each have 100 sheets of paper. How many
   sheets of paper does Carter have in all?

   Carter has _____ sheets of paper in all.

Write About It

7. A teacher asked the class to write seven hundred
   sixty as hundreds, tens, and ones. Kylie wrote
   6 hundreds, 16 tens, 0 ones. Sarah wrote
   7 hundreds, 6 tens, 0 ones. Whose answer
   is correct? Explain.

   _____

   _____

Place Value in Three-Digit Numbers

Objective
- Identify the place value of digits in numbers to 999.

Math Words
digit
hundreds
tens
ones

Henry scored 254 points in a game.
What is the value of each digit in 254?

To tell the value of each digit in a number, look at its place in the number.

hundreds	tens	ones
2	5	4

2 5 4

The 2 is in the hundreds place.

The 5 is in the tens place.

The 4 is in the ones place.

Its value is 200.

Its value is 50.

Its value is 4.

PRACTICE

Circle the value of the underlined digit.

1. 56<u>8</u>

    8   80   800

2. 5<u>0</u>9

    5   50   500

3. 9<u>4</u>5

    4   40   400

4. Write a three-digit number that has a 4 in the hundreds place.

    _____

    What is the value of the 4 in your number? _____

Write the value of the underlined digit.

5. 6̲83	6. 25̲0	7. 3̲17	8. 50̲9
_____	_____	_____	_____
9. 7̲35	10. 9̲72	11. 84̲9	12. 1̲27
_____	_____	_____	_____

Use the numbers in the box for Exercises 13–14.

| 348 | 403 | 834 |

13. Which number has a digit 4 with a value of 40? _____

14. Which number has a digit 3 with a value of 3? _____

Problem Solving

15. At a baseball game, the coach brings a water bottle for each of his players. How many water bottles do you think he brings? Circle the best answer.

    2   20   200

Remember, a digit's place in a number determines its value.

Write About It

16. Dave wrote the number 286. He thinks the value of the 2 is less than the value of the 8 because 2 is less than 8. Is Dave correct? Explain.

_____

_____

LESSON 7-3

Name_____

Place Value in Three-Digit Numbers

To tell the value of each digit in a number,
look at its place in the number.

Find the value of each digit in the number 254.

hundreds	tens	ones
2	5	4

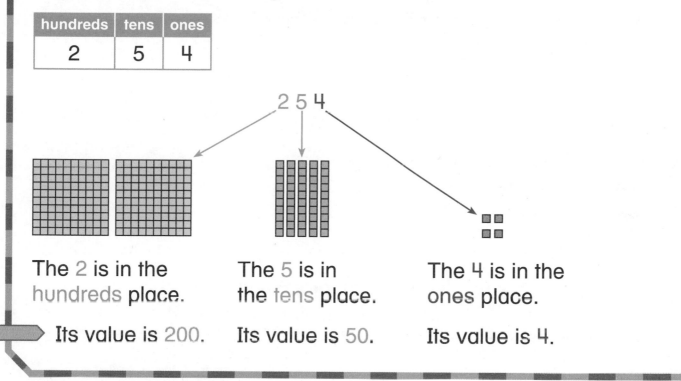

The 2 is in the
hundreds place.

The 5 is in
the tens place.

The 4 is in the
ones place.

Its value is 200.

Its value is 50.

Its value is 4.

MORE PRACTICE

Circle the value of the underlined digit.

1. 1<u>4</u>2

    4   40   400

2. 36<u>1</u>

    1   10   100

3. <u>8</u>14

    8   80   800

4. Write a three-digit number that has a digit 6
in the ones place.

_____

What is the value of the 6 in your number? _____

Write the value of the underlined digit.

1. 2<u>5</u>0 _____

2. 80<u>3</u> _____

3. <u>3</u>18 _____

4. 42<u>6</u> _____

Use the numbers in the box for Exercises 5–6.

| 158 | 581 | 815 |

5. Which number has a 5 with a value of 5? _____

6. Which number has a 1 with a value of 100? _____

Problem Solving

7. At a carnival, Melissa buys large pretzels for herself and her friends. How many pretzels do you think she buys? Circle the best answer.

   5   50   500

Write About It

8. A fruit stand sells red and green apples. Each type of apple comes in packages of 10 apples and packages of 1 apple. Carl buys 4 packages of red apples and 3 packages of green apples. Can you tell if Carl has more red apples or green apples? Explain.

   _____

   _____

   _____

Expanded Form with Hundreds, Tens, and Ones

Bailey has 3 boxes of 100 craft sticks, 8 boxes of 10 craft sticks, and 5 single craft sticks. How many craft sticks does Bailey have?

3 boxes of 100   8 boxes of 10   5 singles

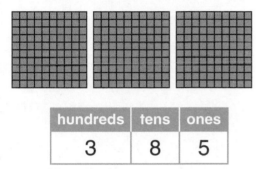

hundreds	tens	ones
3	8	5

Use expanded form to find the number.
Write an addition equation that adds the values of the digits in the number.

$$300 + 80 + 5 = 385$$

expanded form

▷ Bailey has 385 craft sticks.

PRACTICE

Write how many hundreds, tens, and ones.
Then write the number in expanded form.

1. 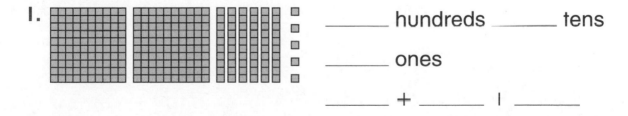 _____ hundreds _____ tens

_____ ones

_____ + _____ | _____

Write each number in expanded form.
Then write the number.

2. 7 hundreds 3 tens 6 ones _____ + _____ + _____ _____

3. 4 hundreds 0 tens 9 ones _____ + _____ + _____ _____

Write the number.

4. $600 + 50 + 1 =$ _____	5. $300 + 8 =$ _____
6. _____ $= 200 + 10 + 4$	7. $800 + 70 + 7 =$ _____
8. $400 + 30 =$ _____	9. _____ $= 100 + 60 + 7$

Problem Solving

10. Kona models a number with 5 hundred flats,
    8 ten rods, and 2 ones units. Then he takes away
    2 hundred flats and adds 5 ones units. What is
    Kona's number now?

    Kona's number is now _____.

Write About It

11. Sadie wrote $50 + 3$ to show the expanded form
    of 503. Is Sadie correct? Explain your reasoning.

    _____

    _____

    _____

Name_____

Expanded Form with Hundreds, Tens, and Ones

To write the expanded form of 385, add the values of each digit.

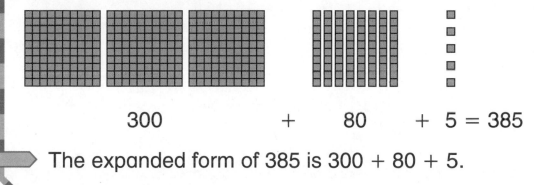

300   +   80   + 5 = 385

▷ The expanded form of 385 is 300 + 80 + 5.

MORE PRACTICE

Fill in the place-value chart. Then write the number in expanded form.

1. 906

hundreds	tens	ones

_____ + _____ + _____

2. 341

hundreds	tens	ones

_____ + _____ + _____

Write each number in expanded form. Then write the number.

3. 2 hundreds 5 tens 4 ones   _____ + _____ + _____   _____

4. 7 hundreds 3 tens 3 ones   _____ + _____ + _____   _____

Fill in the place-value chart. Then write the number in expanded form.

1. 785

hundreds	tens	ones

_____ + _____ + _____

2. 429

hundreds	tens	ones

_____ + _____ + _____

**Write each number in expanded form.
Then write the number.**

3. 8 hundreds 0 tens 1 one   _____ + _____ + _____   _____

4. 5 hundreds 6 tens 8 ones   _____ + _____ + _____   _____

Problem Solving

5. A number has 2 ones, 2 more hundreds than ones, and 5 more tens than hundreds. What is the number? Write it in expanded form.

The number is _____.

The expanded form is _____.

Write About It

6. Trevor ran 425 meters in gym class. He wrote 4 + 2 + 5 to show the expanded form of 425. Is he correct? Explain your reasoning.

_____

_____

_____

Name _____

Write the number.

1. 30 tens = ____ hundreds

2. 600 = _____ ones

Write the number and the number name.
Group tens to make hundreds if needed.

3. 2 hundreds 22 tens 6 ones

   _____   _____

4. 5 hundreds 13 tens 2 ones

   _____   _____

5. 3 hundreds 51 tens 0 ones

   _____   _____

Write the value of the underlined digit.

6. <u>3</u>08

   _____

7. 18<u>4</u>

   _____

8. <u>5</u>60

   _____

9. 9<u>2</u>7

   _____

Use the numbers in the box for Exercises 10–12.

| 257 | 572 | 705 |

10. Which number has a digit 7 with a value of 70? _____

11. Which number has a digit 5 with a value of 5? _____

12. Which number has a digit 2 with a value of 200? _____

**Write each number in expanded form.
Then write the number.**

13. 2 hundreds 1 ten 6 ones _____ + ____ + ____ _____

14. 5 hundreds 3 tens 4 ones _____ + ____ + ____ _____

15. 9 hundreds 0 tens 2 ones _____ + ____ + ____ _____

Write the number.

16. 300 + 50 = _____

17. _____ = 700 + 10 + 4

18. _____ = 100 + 60 + 8

19. 800 + 1 = _____

Solve.

20. There are 4 boxes of 100 bolts, 30 packs of 10 bolts, and 7 single bolts in a tool shed. How many bolts are there in all?

_____ bolts

21. A teacher makes a name tag for each of her students. How many name tags do you think she makes? Circle the best answer.

3   30   300

22. Ling writes a number that has 3 ones, 1 more hundred than ones, and 3 more tens than hundreds. What is her number?

Ling's number is now _____.

Skip Count Within 1000

Lia has 5 red cards worth 5 points each,
8 yellow cards worth 10 points each, and
6 green cards worth 100 points each.

Objective
- Skip count by 5s, 10s, and 100s within 1000.

Math Word
skip count

How many points is each set of cards worth?

Skip count 5 red cards by 5s: 5, 10, 15, 20, 25.

Skip count 8 yellow cards by 10s: 10, 20, 30, 40, 50, 60, 70, 80.

Skip count 6 green cards by 100s: 100, 200, 300, 400, 500, 600.

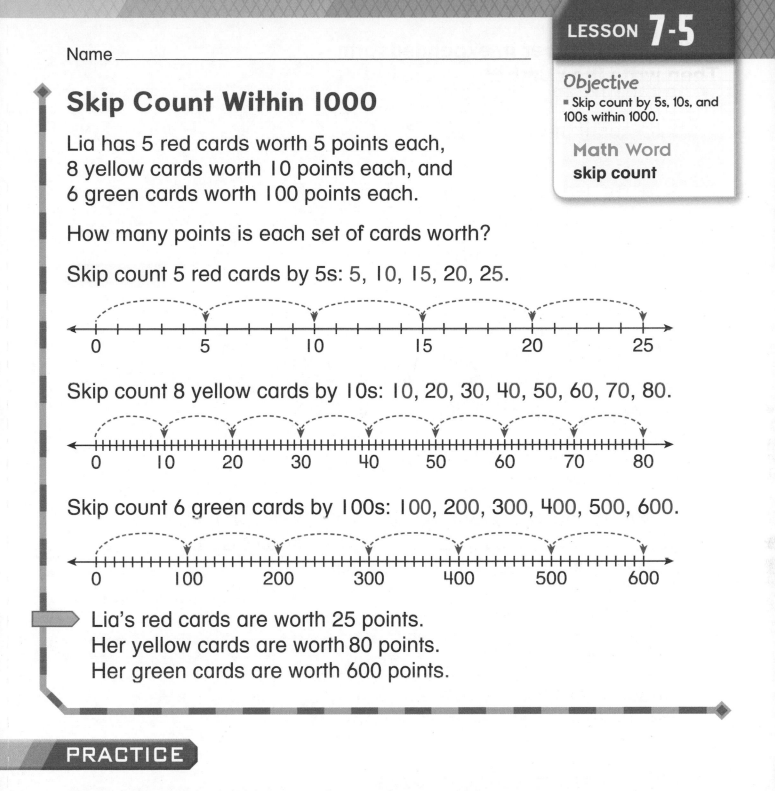

Lia's red cards are worth 25 points.
Her yellow cards are worth 80 points.
Her green cards are worth 600 points.

PRACTICE

Skip count by 5s. Write the missing numbers.

1.

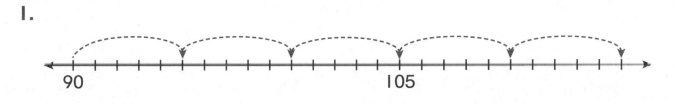

90   105

_____   _____   _____   _____

Write the missing numbers.

2. Skip count by 5s.   730, 735, _____, _____, _____, 755, _____

3. Skip count by 10s.   350, 360, _____, 380, _____, _____, _____

4. Skip count by 100s. 400, 500, _____, _____, 800, _____, _____

Problem Solving

5. Kylee's art teacher buys 7 boxes of buttons.
Each box has 100 buttons in it.
How many buttons are there in all?

There are _____ buttons in all.

6. Cesar has 9 cards worth 10 points each. Devon has
15 cards worth 5 points each. Whose cards have the
greater value? Explain your reasoning.

_____

_____

_____

Write About It

7. Lucy wanted to skip count by 5s.
The numbers she said were 5, 15, 25, 35, and 45.
Is Lucy correct? Explain your answer.

_____

_____

Name_____

Skip Count Within 1000

You can skip count by 5s, 10s, or 100s and find patterns in the numbers.

Skip count by 5s: 5, 10, 15, 20, 25.

Skip count by 10s: 10, 20, 30, 40, 50, 60, 70, 80.

Skip count by 100s: 100, 200, 300, 400, 500, 600.

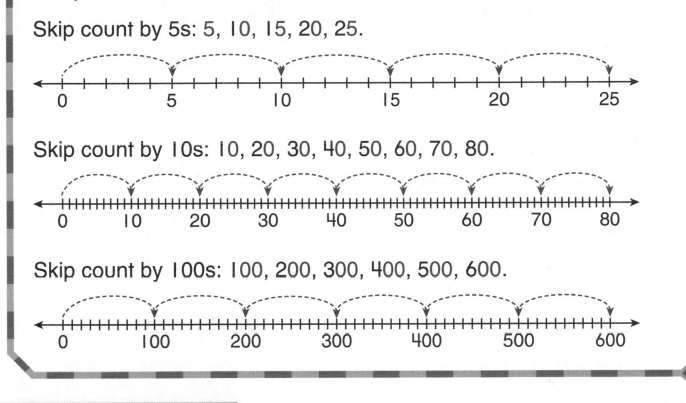

MORE PRACTICE

Write the missing numbers.

1. Skip count by 10s.

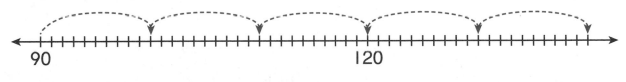

90   120

_____ _____ _____ _____

2. Skip count by 5s.

145   150

_____ _____ _____

Write the missing numbers.

1. Skip count by 5s. 380, 385, _____, _____, _____, _____, 410

2. Skip count by 10s. 280, 290, _____, _____, _____, _____, 340

3. Skip count by 100s. _____, _____, 300, 400, _____, _____, _____

Write the correct number.

4. When you start at 0 and skip count by ____s, the ones digit of each number is either 0 or 5.

5. When you start at 0 and skip count by _____s or

    _____s, the ones digit of each number is 0.

Problem Solving

6. Amy has 12 boxes of pens. There are 10 pens in each box. How many pens does Amy have in all?

   Amy has _____ pens in all.

Write About It

7. Gavin skip counts by 5s from 0 and Luis skip counts by 10s from 0. Not counting 0, what are the first three numbers that **both** boys say? Explain the pattern in the numbers they both say.

   _____

   _____

Name _____

Compare Numbers Within 1000

Jacob walks 234 steps to the lunchroom. Ryan walks 312 steps, Tyler walks 234 steps, and Noah walks 229 steps. Compare Jacob's steps to each friend's steps.

Use <, =, or > . Compare 234 to each number.

234 and 312	**234 and 234**	**234 and 229**
Compare the hundreds.	The hundreds, tens, and ones are the same.	The hundreds are the same. Compare the tens.
2 hundreds is fewer than 3 hundreds.	The numbers are equal.	3 tens is more than 2 tens.
234 is less than 312.	234 is equal to 234.	234 is greater than 229.
234 < 312	234 = 234	234 > 229
Jacob walks fewer steps than Ryan.	Jacob and Tyler walk the same number of steps.	Jacob walks more steps than Noah.

PRACTICE

Compare. Write *is less than*, *is equal to*, or *is greater than*. Then write <, =, or >.

A number with fewer digits than another is always the lesser number.

1. 815 _____ 809

   815 ◯ 809

2. 98 _____ 103

   98 ◯ 103

Compare. Write <, =, or >.

3. 308 ◯ 705	4. 986 ◯ 982	5. 264 ◯ 264
6. 641 ◯ 641	7. 156 ◯ 158	8. 414 ◯ 405
9. 724 ◯ 716	10. 837 ◯ 837	11. 553 ◯ 554

Problem Solving

12. Sarah has a shelf that is 175 centimeters long.
She has a model ship that is 146 centimeters long.
Will the model ship fit on Sarah's shelf? Explain.

_____

_____

_____

Write About It

13. When you compare two three-digit numbers why is it important to compare the digits in the hundreds place before you compare the digits in the tens place?

_____

_____

_____

Name_____

Compare Numbers Within 1000

To compare three-digit numbers, start with the digits in the hundreds place.

Use <, =, or > .

Compare 234 and 312.	**Compare 234 and 234.**	**Compare 234 and 229.**
Compare the hundreds.	The hundreds, tens, and ones are the same.	The hundreds are the same. Compare the tens.
2 hundreds is fewer than 3 hundreds.	The numbers are equal.	3 tens is more than 2 tens.
234 is less than 312.	234 is equal to 234.	234 is greater than 229.
234 < 312	234 = 234	234 > 229

MORE PRACTICE

Compare. Write *is less than*, *is equal to*, or *is greater than*. Then write <, =, or >.

1. 405 _____ 407

   405 ◯ 407

2. 129 _____ 129

   129 ◯ 129

3. 357 _____ 409

   357 ◯ 409

4. 236 _____ 228

   236 ◯ 228

Compare. Write <, =, or >.

1. 516 ◯ 543	2. 806 ◯ 647	3. 939 ◯ 939
4. 257 ◯ 261	5. 137 ◯ 119	6. 304 ◯ 307
7. 615 ◯ 615	8. 492 ◯ 497	9. 834 ◯ 814

Problem Solving

10. Brianna's address has a number that is greater than 659 but less than 665. What could be the number of her address?

    Brianna's address could be number _____.

Write About It

11. Oliver thinks that 756 > 763 because 756 has more ones than 763. Jalen thinks that 763 > 756 because 763 has more tens than 756. Who is correct? Explain.

    _____

    _____

    _____

    _____

    _____

Name _____

Order Numbers Within 1000

This month Jada read 178 pages, Erin read 126 pages, and Molly read 172 pages. What is the order of the numbers from least to greatest?

- Compare the hundreds: 178   126   172
  The hundreds are all the same.

- Compare the tens: 178   126   172
  126 has the fewest tens, so it is the least number.
  178 and 172 have the same number of tens.

- Compare the ones: 178   172
  178 has more ones, so it is the greatest number.

  The numbers from least to greatest are 126, 172, 178.

You can also write numbers in order from greatest to least. Write the greatest number first and the least number last.

  The numbers from greatest to least are 178, 172, 126.

PRACTICE

Write the numbers in order from least to greatest.

1. 375   126   704   259

   126, _____, _____, _____

2. 530   472   509   498

   472, _____, _____, _____

3. 914   907   927   908

   _____, _____, _____, _____

4. 671   176   617   167

   _____, _____, _____, _____

Use the numbers in the box for Exercises 5–6.

| 248 | 401 | 234 | 305 |

5. Which is the greatest number? _____

6. Did you use the hundreds, tens,
   or ones to decide which number is greatest? _____

Write a number to complete the list of numbers from least to greatest.

7. 237, _____, 549, 791

8. 416, 458, _____, 472

Problem Solving

Use the table to answer the problem.

9. On which day was the greatest number
   of cans collected for the recycling drive?

   _____

Recycling Drive Cans Collected	
Monday	505
Tuesday	450
Wednesday	405
Thursday	550

Write About It

10. Connor says the numbers 610, 712, 720,
    and 629 are in order from least to greatest.
    Is he correct? Explain.

    _____

    _____

    _____

Name _____

Order Numbers Within 1000

Write the numbers 178, 126, and 172 in order
from least to greatest and from greatest to least.

- Compare the hundreds: 178   126   172
  The hundreds are all the same.

- Compare the tens: 178   126   172
  126 has the fewest tens, so it is the least number.
  178 and 172 have the same number of tens.

- Compare the ones: 178   172
  178 has more ones, so it is the greatest number.

> The numbers from least to greatest are
> 126, 172, 178.

> The numbers from greatest to least are
> 178, 172, 126.

MORE PRACTICE

Write the numbers in order from least to greatest.

1. 314   325   319   317

   314, _____, _____, _____

2. 409   405   399   401

   399, _____, _____, _____

Write the numbers in order from greatest to least.

3. 314   304   431   413

   431, _____, _____, _____

4. 992   492   504   919

   992, _____, _____, _____

Write the numbers in order from least to greatest.

1. 641   302   802   504

———, ———, ———, ———

2. 855   885   807   870

———, ———, ———, ———

Write the numbers in order from greatest to least.

3. 614   164   461   416

———, ———, ———, ———

4. 712   702   721   720

———, ———, ———, ———

Problem Solving

5. George's house number is 814, Alex's house number is 418, Kai's house number is 148, and Josh's house number is 841. What is the order of their house numbers from greatest to least?

_____

Write About It

6. A teacher asks his class to complete the list of numbers from least to greatest.

   243, ———, 284, 303

   Ruby says the missing number must have 2 hundreds. Jasmin says the missing number can have 2 hundreds or 3 hundreds. Who is correct? Explain.

   _____

   _____

Problem Solving Read〉Plan〉Solve〉Check
Use a Table

A fruit stand sold 133 peaches, 167 apples, 138 bananas, and 159 mangoes. List the fruits in order from greatest to least number sold.

You can use a table to compare numbers more easily.

The columns of the table tell the **fruit** and the **number sold**. There are 4 kinds of fruit, so there are 4 rows.

Fruit	Number Sold
Peaches	133
Apples	167
Bananas	138
Mangoes	159

The numbers are lined up in the Number Sold column, showing how the digits compare.
All the numbers have 1 hundred, so compare the tens.

The greatest number of tens is 6 in 167.

- Apples were sold the most: 167.

- Mangoes have the next greatest number: 159.

The numbers of peaches and bananas sold have the same number of tens. Compare the ones.

- Bananas are next with 138 sold.

- Peaches were sold the least: 133.

> The fruits listed from greatest to least number sold are apples, mangoes, bananas, and peaches.

Use the table to answer Exercises 1–4.

School Supply	Number Ordered
Pencils	640
Pens	
Erasers	510
Glue Sticks	

1. A school store ordered 640 pencils, 730 pens, 510 erasers, and 450 glue sticks. Fill in the missing numbers in the table.

2. Did the school store order more erasers or glue sticks?

   The school store ordered more _____.

3. Did the school store order fewer pencils or pens?

   The school store ordered fewer _____.

4. What is the order of school supplies from least to greatest number ordered?

   _____

Write About It

5. Jonah's family drove 325 miles on Thursday, 202 miles on Friday, and 411 miles on Saturday. He made this table to show the information.

Day	Miles

   What did Jonah do wrong? Explain what he needs to do to fix the table before he can fill in the information.

   _____

   _____

   _____

Name_____

Problem Solving
Use a Table

A fruit stand sold 133 peaches, 167 apples, 138 bananas, and 159 mangoes.

List the fruits in order from greatest to least number sold.

You can organize information from a problem in a table.

A table helps you compare numbers more easily.

Fruit	Number Sold
Peaches	133
Apples	167
Bananas	138
Mangoes	159

Compare the numbers to order the information.

- First compare the numbers in the hundreds place. All the numbers have 1 in the hundreds place.

- Compare the numbers in the tens place. 167 has the greatest number of tens.

- Then compare the numbers in the ones place. 133 has the fewest number of ones.

- The numbers in order from greatest to least are: 167, 159, 138, and 133.

> The fruits sold from greatest to least are apples, mangoes, bananas, and peaches.

Use the table to answer Problems 1–5.

Season	Votes
	21
Winter	27
Spring	

1. A group of second-grade students voted for their favorite season. 21 chose fall, 27 chose winter, 12 chose spring, and 45 chose summer. Fill in the missing information in the table.

2. What season did the least number of students choose?

   The least number of students chose _____.

3. Which season did the greatest number of students choose?

   The greatest number of students chose _____.

4. Which seasons had more votes, fall or winter? Explain how you know.

   _____

   _____

   _____

5. Write the seasons in order from least to greatest number of votes. Explain how you can use the table to help you.

   _____

   _____

   _____

   _____

HOMEWORK

Use the table to answer Problems 1–4.

1. A farmer picked 328 beans, 387 carrots, and 321 peppers. Fill in the missing information in the table.

Vegetable	Number Picked
	328
Carrots	

2. Did the farmer pick more beans or peppers?

   The farmer picked more _____.

3. What vegetable did the farmer pick the least number of?

   The farmer picked the least number of _____.

4. What is the order of the vegetables from greatest to least number picked?

   _____

Read the problem and solve.

5. Amy skip counts by 5s from 400 to 500. Gianna skip counts by 10s from 400 to 500. What numbers do both girls say?

   Both girls say _____

   _____

Use the table to answer Problems 6–8.

Toy	Number Sold
Robots	753
Games	758

6. A toy store sold 739 cars, 753 robots, 732 dolls, and 758 games. Fill in the missing information in the table.

7. Did the toy store sell fewer cars or robots?

   The toy store sold fewer _____.

8. List the toys from least to greatest number sold.

   _____

Read the problem and solve.

9. Emily is thinking of a number. She says, "The value of the hundreds digit is 800. The digit in the ones place is greater than 3 but less than 5. The sum of all three digits is 13." What is Emily's number?

   Emily's number is _____.

—Write About It—

10. Write the greatest possible three-digit number using the digits 5, 3, and 6. Explain your reasoning.

   _____

   _____

   _____

Write the number.

1. 20 tens = _____ ones | 2. 9 hundreds = _____ tens

Write the number and the number name.
Group tens to make hundreds if needed.

3. 4 hundreds 32 tens 6 ones

_____   _____

Write the value of the underlined digit.

4. 5$\underline{1}$4 | 5. $\underline{3}$61 | 6. 9$\underline{4}$7 | 7. 40$\underline{5}$

_____ | _____ | _____ | _____

Solve.

8. Max buys enough pizza slices for everyone in his class to have at a party. How many slices do you think he buys? Circle the best answer.

4   40   400

Write the value in expanded form.
Then write the number.

9. 7 hundreds 4 tens 6 ones

_____ + _____ + _____   _____

10. 1 hundred 0 tens 5 ones _____ + ____ + ____   _____

Use number patterns to skip count.
Write the missing numbers.

11. Skip count by 5s.   315, 320, _____, _____, _____, _____, 345

12. Skip count by 10s.   180, 190, _____, _____, _____, 230, _____

Compare. Write <, =, or >.

13. 259 ◯ 295   14. 106 ◯ 104   15. 234 ◯ 234

16. 308 ◯ 307   17. 832 ◯ 732   18. 615 ◯ 651

Write the numbers in order from greatest to least.

19. 583   235   798   740   20. 673   367   763   736

_____, _____, _____, _____   _____, _____, _____, _____

Use the table to answer the questions.

21. Are there more students
in Grade 1 or Grade 3?

There are more students in

_____ than in _____.

Grade	Number of Students
Grade 1	158
Grade 2	137
Grade 3	154
Grade 4	162

22. What is the order of the grades from least to
greatest number of students?

_____

Name_____

**Lake Mead was formed when the
Hoover Dam was built. It is a man-made lake.**

1. The size of Lake Mead, in square miles,
   can be written as 1 hundred 14 tens 8 ones.
   Write the size of Lake Mead as a number.

   _____ square miles

2. Write the size of Lake Mead in expanded form.

   _____ square miles

3. A drought shrinks the size of the lake by 3 tens.
   What is the size of Lake Mead during the drought?

   _____ square miles

4. Find out more about Lake Mead and the Hoover Dam.
   Why were they made? What are they used for?

   _____

   _____

5. Research other man-made lakes around the United
   States and the world. Find information such as:

   • What is the size of the lake? Was the lake made
     by building a dam? What is the lake used for?

   • How does the size of the lake compare to
     Lake Mead's size?

   Share your findings with your classmates.

Name _____

Determine the best answer for each problem.

1. Add.

$7 + 9 =$ _____

2. Subtract.

$12 - 4 =$ _____

3. Add.

$$\begin{array}{r} 5 \\ + \ 7 \\ \hline \end{array}$$

4. Subtract.

$$\begin{array}{r} 14 \\ - \ 9 \\ \hline \end{array}$$

5. Add.

$$\begin{array}{r} 4 \\ 8 \\ + \ 3 \\ \hline \end{array}$$

6. Add.

$$\begin{array}{r} 6 \\ 3 \\ + \ 9 \\ \hline \end{array}$$

7. What is the value of the 1 in 814?

A. one

B. ten

C. one hundred

8. How many hundreds are in 632?

A. 2 hundreds

B. 3 hundreds

C. 6 hundreds

9. Which answer is equal to 307?

A. $3 + 0 + 7$

B. $300 + 7$

C. $30 + 7$

10. Which answer is equal to 955?

A. $900 + 50 + 5$

B. $9 + 5 + 5$

C. $9 + 55$

Addition: Three-Digit Numbers

In 1903, Orville and Wilbur Wright first flew an airplane. Since then people have been making airplanes that fly faster and go farther. Today, airplanes have many different shapes and sizes.

Winging It

♦ The Wright brothers' plane had a 40-foot wingspan. Today a big passenger plane can have a 262-foot wingspan.

Big Planes, Big Buildings

♦ Large planes are built in very large buildings. One airplane factory is so large that about 55 soccer fields could fit inside it! How big do you think the factory doors need to be for jumbo planes to get through them?

Dear Family,

In this chapter, we will learn about adding three-digit numbers.

Here are the key **Math Words** for this chapter:

count on	**ones**
sum	**tens**
addend	**hundreds**
place value	**regroup**

Terms such as *ones, tens, hundreds,* and *addend* are not new to students. Some Math Words are repeated, as they set a foundation for students' understanding of and fluency with addition. Use the glossary to find the definition of each word and help your child make flash cards.

During this chapter about adding three-digit numbers, we will also be making STEAM (Science, Technology, Engineering, the Arts, and Mathematics) connections about airplanes and wingspan. Read the opening to the chapter together.

Keep Your Skills Sharp

Here is a **Keep Your Skills Sharp** activity to do at home to prepare for this chapter.

Play number riddles with your child. One player thinks of a three-digit number and gives clues to the other player. For example, "My number has a 5 in the hundreds place, a tens digit with a value of 80, and a ones digit that is 1 more than the hundreds digit. What is my number?" (586) Be sure to switch roles.

Mental Math: Add 1, 10, or 100

Three farms each have 240 sheep.
Farm A buys 1 more sheep,
Farm B buys 10 more sheep, and
Farm C buys 100 more sheep.
How many sheep does each farm have now?

You can count on mentally to add.

$240 + 1 = ?$	$240 + 10 = ?$	$240 + 100 = ?$
Count on 1.	Count on 10.	Count on 100.
240, 241	240, 250	240, 340

$240 + 1 = 241 \qquad 240 + 10 = 250 \qquad 240 + 100 = 340$

Farm A has 241 sheep, Farm B has 250 sheep, and Farm C has 340 sheep now.

PRACTICE

Count on 1.

1. 450, _____
2. 167, _____
3. 524, _____
4. 679, _____

Count on 10.

5. 381, _____
6. 214, _____
7. 940, _____
8. 706, _____

Count on 100.

9. 267, _____
10. 885, _____
11. 736, _____
12. 608, _____

Match the pattern to its description.

13. 435, 535, 635, 735   + 10

14. 618, 619, 620, 621   + 1

15. 933, 943, 953, 963   + 100

> Find the digit that changes in each number in the pattern. Its place value will help you choose the correct description.

Continue the pattern. Write + 1, + 10, or + 100 to explain the pattern.

16. 319, 329, 339, _____   Pattern: _____

17. 298, 398, 498, _____   Pattern: _____

18. 527, 528, 529, _____   Pattern: _____

Problem Solving

19. Brooke scores 462 points playing a game. Ashley's score is 10 points more than Brooke's score. Shima's score is 100 points more than Ashley's score. How many points did Shima score?

   Shima scored _____ points.

Write About It

20. Brandon says he does not need to add to know which is more, 673 + 10 or 673 + 100. Is Brandon correct? Explain why or why not.

   _____

   _____

   _____

Name _____

Mental Math: Add 1, 10, or 100

You can count on mentally to add 1, 10, or 100.

$240 + 1 = ?$	$240 + 10 = ?$	$240 + 100 = ?$
Count on 1.	Count on 10.	Count on 100.
240, 241	240, 250	240, 340

$240 + 1 = 241$ $240 + 10 = 250$ $240 + 100 = 340$

MORE PRACTICE

Count on 1.

1. 281, _____ | 2. 759, _____ | 3. 483, _____ | 4. 679, _____

Count on 10.

5. 368, _____ | 6. 502, _____ | 7. 846, _____ | 8. 183, _____

Count on 100.

9. 560, _____ | 10. 386, _____ | 11. 304, _____ | 12. 772, _____

Add.

13. $627 + 1 = $ _____   14. $538 + 10 = $ _____

15. $251 + 100 = $ _____   16. $839 + 1 = $ _____

Add.

1. 842 + 100 = _____

2. 512 + 10 = _____

3. 936 + 1 = _____

4. 485 + 10 = _____

Continue the pattern. Write + 1, + 10, or + 100 to explain the pattern.

5. 467, 477, 487, _____   Pattern: _____

6. 371, 471, 571, _____   Pattern: _____

7. 357, 358, 359, _____   Pattern: _____

Problem Solving

8. School A has 578 students. School B has 10 more students than School A. School C has 100 more students than School B. How many students does School C have?

   School C has _____ students.

Write About It

9. Joseph makes a number pattern with three-digit numbers. The tens digit increases by 1 each time. What is Joseph's pattern? Explain how you know.

   _____

   _____

   _____

Name_____

Add Hundreds, Tens, and Ones

There are 133 people in line at the water park. Then 24 more people get in line. How many people are in line now?

Look at the place-value model for this problem.

Objective
- Add three-digit numbers without regrouping.

Math Words
sum
addend
place value
ones
tens
hundreds

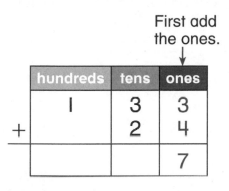

hundreds	tens	ones

Add 133 + 24 to find the sum. Line up the addends by place value.

First add the ones. ↓

hundreds	tens	ones
1	3	3
+	2	4
		7

Next add the tens. ↓

hundreds	tens	ones
1	3	3
+	2	4
	5	7

Then add the hundreds. ↓

hundreds	tens	ones
1	3	3
+	2	4
1	5	7

➤ There are 157 people in line now.

PRACTICE

Add. Start with the ones.

1. ↓

hundreds	tens	ones
4	6	4
+ 1	2	1

2. ↓

hundreds	tens	ones
7	2	4
+ 2	5	3

3. ↓

hundreds	tens	ones
8	6	3
+	1	0

Add.

4. $\begin{array}{r} 210 \\ +322 \end{array}$	**5.** $\begin{array}{r} 331 \\ +164 \end{array}$	**6.** $\begin{array}{r} 600 \\ +\ \ 73 \end{array}$	**7.** $\begin{array}{r} 435 \\ +414 \end{array}$
8. $\begin{array}{r} 310 \\ +350 \end{array}$	**9.** $\begin{array}{r} 603 \\ +304 \end{array}$	**10.** $\begin{array}{r} 113 \\ +764 \end{array}$	**11.** $\begin{array}{r} 274 \\ +602 \end{array}$

Circle the correct sum.

12. $752 + 30 =$ _____   762   772   782

13. $425 + 163 =$ _____   488   588   688

Problem Solving

14. A carnival sells 204 tickets on Monday. It sells 131 more tickets on Tuesday than on Monday. How many tickets does the carnival sell in all on those two days? Use the place-value chart to show your work.

	hundreds	tens	ones
+			

The carnival sells _____ tickets in all.

Write About It

15. Erin adds $353 + 125$. Explain the mistake she made. Then tell the correct sum.

$\begin{array}{r} 353 \\ +125 \\ \hline 438 \end{array}$

_____

_____

Name _____

Add Hundreds, Tens, and Ones

133 + 24 = ?

Look at the place value model for this problem.

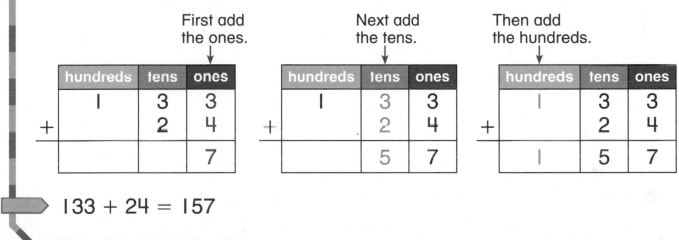

To find the sum, you can line up the addends by place value.

First add the ones.		
hundreds	tens	ones
1	3	3
	2	4
+		
		7

Next add the tens.		
hundreds	tens	ones
1	3	3
	2	4
+		
	5	7

Then add the hundreds.		
hundreds	tens	ones
1	3	3
	2	4
+		
1	5	7

➤ 133 + 24 = 157

MORE PRACTICE

Add. Start with the ones.

1.

hundreds	tens	ones ↓
3	4	7
3	2	1
+		

2.

hundreds	tens	ones ↓
6	1	6
2	3	2
+		

3.

hundreds	tens	ones ↓
5	2	3
	6	1
+		

Add.

1. 324
   +124

2. 480
   +101

3. 112
   + 84

4. 113
   +753

5. 460
   +300

6. 403
   +234

7. 640
   +152

8. 214
   +370

Circle the correct sum.

9. 612 + 50 = _____   642   652   662

10. 304 + 471 = _____   675   775   875

Problem Solving

11. A cafeteria served 243 apples at lunch.
    It served 102 more oranges than apples. How
    many apples and oranges were served in all?

    The cafeteria served _____ apples and
    oranges in all.

Write About It

12. Jake adds 216 + 42. Explain the mistake
    he made. Then tell the correct sum.

    216
    + 42
    636

    _____

    _____

    _____

Name _____

Add: Regroup Ones as Tens

It is Election Day in a small town.
347 people voted in the morning.
225 people voted in the afternoon.
How many people voted in all?

Add 347 + 225.

Look at the model.

Notice that there are
more than 9 ones.
You will need to regroup
when adding the ones.

Objective
■ Add three-digit numbers, regrouping ones as tens.

Math Words
sum
addend
regroup
ones
tens
hundreds

- Line up the addends by place value.

- Add the ones. Regroup 10 ones as 1 ten.

- Add the regrouped ten to the tens place.

- Add the tens and then the hundreds.

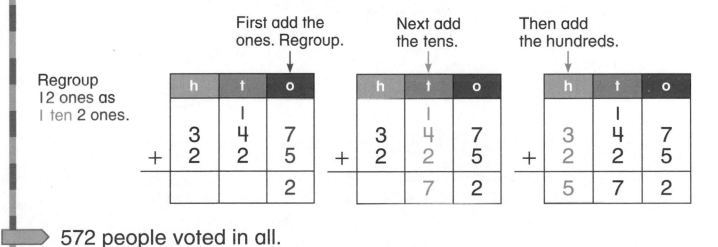

Regroup
12 ones as
1 ten 2 ones.

First add the ones. Regroup.

h	t	o
	1	
3	4	7
+ 2	2	5
		2

Next add the tens.

h	t	o
	1	
3	4	7
+ 2	2	5
	7	2

Then add the hundreds.

h	t	o
	1	
3	4	7
+ 2	2	5
5	7	2

> 572 people voted in all.

Add. Regroup where needed.

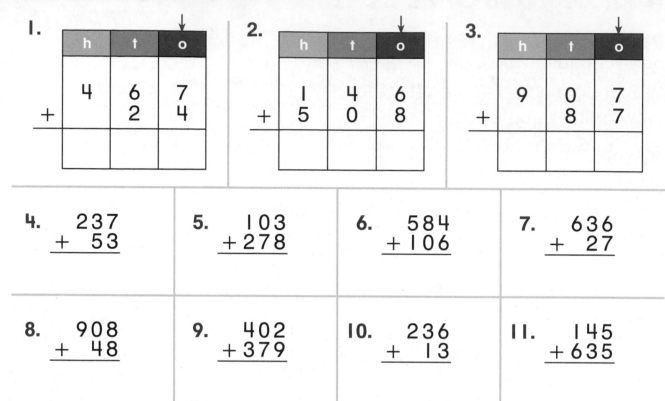

1.
h	t	o
4	6	7
+	2	4

2.
h	t	o
1	4	6
+ 5	0	8

3.
h	t	o
9	0	7
+	8	7

4.   237
   + 53

5.   103
   +278

6.   584
   +106

7.   636
   + 27

8.   908
   + 48

9.   402
   +379

10.   236
   + 13

11.   145
   +635

Problem Solving

12. A band has 374 members. If 18 new members sign up, how many members will there be?

There will be _____ members.

Write About It

13. Use the table to answer the question. Which two scores will need regrouping when you add them? Explain.

Player	Score
Austin	155
Kevin	323
David	236

_____

_____

_____

Name_____

Add: Regroup Ones as Tens

347 + 225 = ?

Look at the model for the problem.

There are more than 9 ones.
Regroup when adding the ones.

To find the sum, you can
line up the addends by
place value.

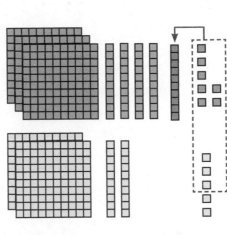

	First add the ones. Regroup.	Next add the tens.	Then add the hundreds.

Regroup
12 ones as
1 ten 2 ones.

h	t	o
	1	
3	4	7
+ 2	2	5
		2

h	t	o
	1	
3	4	7
+ 2	2	5
	7	2

h	t	o
	1	
3	4	7
+ 2	2	5
5	7	2

347 + 225 = 572

MORE PRACTICE

Add. Regroup where needed.

1.

h	t	o
6	4	7
+ 1	4	5

2.

h	t	o
3	0	5
+ 6	8	5

3.

h	t	o
1	3	9
+ 5	4	3

Add. Regroup where needed.

1. $\begin{array}{r} 245 \\ +535 \\ \hline \end{array}$	2. $\begin{array}{r} 460 \\ +336 \\ \hline \end{array}$	3. $\begin{array}{r} 657 \\ +\ 28 \\ \hline \end{array}$	4. $\begin{array}{r} 322 \\ +269 \\ \hline \end{array}$
5. $\begin{array}{r} 712 \\ +244 \\ \hline \end{array}$	6. $\begin{array}{r} 363 \\ +508 \\ \hline \end{array}$	7. $\begin{array}{r} 257 \\ +106 \\ \hline \end{array}$	8. $\begin{array}{r} 604 \\ +191 \\ \hline \end{array}$

Circle the correct sum.

9. $186 + 307 =$ _____   473   483   493

10. $431 + 219 =$ _____   630   640   650

Problem Solving

11. Lydia's family drove 237 miles on Saturday and 218 miles on Sunday. How many miles did they drive in all?

Lydia's family drove _____ miles in all.

Write About It

12. Lauren reads 2 books. She reads a total of 151 pages. Which two books does Lauren read? Explain how you found your answer.

Book	Pages
Lions	45
Rainbows	38
Soccer	113

_____

_____

_____

Regroup Tens as Hundreds Using Models

Objective
- Regroup tens to make a new hundred.

Math Words
regroup
model
ones
tens
hundreds

Jared brings 2 packages of 100 napkins to a picnic. Cody brings 13 packages of 10 napkins and 9 single napkins. How many napkins do they bring to the picnic in all?

Model 2 hundreds, 13 tens, and 9 ones.

There are more than 9 tens. You can regroup the tens.

10 tens = 1 hundred
Regroup 10 tens as 1 hundred.

2 hundreds 13 tens 9 ones = 3 hundreds 3 tens 9 ones

▷ Jared and Cody bring 339 napkins in all.

PRACTICE

Regroup. Write the new number of hundreds, tens, and ones.

1.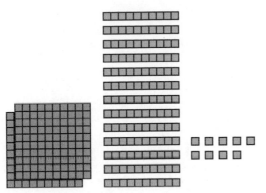

2 hundreds 11 tens 5 ones =

____ hundreds ____ ten

____ ones

Regroup the tens. Write the new number of hundreds, tens, and ones.

2. 2 hundreds 11 tens 1 one = _____ hundreds _____ ten _____ one

3. 8 hundreds 15 tens 6 ones = _____ hundreds _____ tens _____ ones

4. 4 hundreds 16 tens 2 ones = _____ hundreds _____ tens _____ ones

5. 7 hundreds 12 tens 9 ones = _____ hundreds _____ tens _____ ones

6. 2 hundreds 18 tens 8 ones = _____ hundreds _____ tens _____ ones

Problem Solving

7. James has 200 baseball cards. He buys 14 more packs of cards. Each pack has 10 cards in it. How many baseball cards does James have now?

   James has _____ baseball cards now.

Write About It

8. Jessica regroups 10 tens in a number as 1 hundred. Now she has 6 hundreds 3 tens 8 ones. How many hundreds, tens, and ones did Jessica start with? Explain how you know.

   _____

   _____

   _____

Name _____

Regroup Tens as Hundreds Using Models

How can you regroup 2 hundreds, 13 tens, and 9 ones?

There are more than 9 tens.
You can regroup the tens.

10 tens = 1 hundred
Regroup 10 tens as 1 hundred.

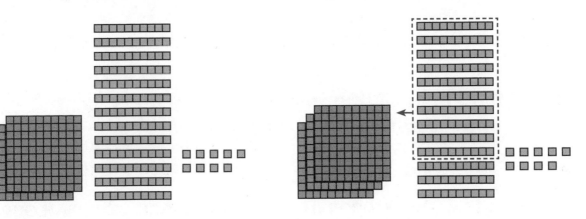

▷ 2 hundreds 13 tens 9 ones = 3 hundreds 3 tens 9 ones

MORE PRACTICE

Regroup the tens. Write the new number of hundreds, tens, and ones.

1. 5 hundreds 11 tens 3 ones = ____ hundreds ____ ten ____ ones

2. 2 hundreds 18 tens 4 ones = ____ hundreds ____ tens ____ ones

3. 7 hundreds 10 tens 5 ones = ____ hundreds ____ tens ____ ones

4. 1 hundred 19 tens 7 ones = ____ hundreds ____ tens ____ ones

5. 2 hundreds 15 tens 0 ones = ____ hundreds ____ tens ____ ones

Regroup the tens. Write the new number of hundreds, tens, and ones.

1. 7 hundreds 14 tens 7 ones = ____ hundreds ____ tens ____ ones

2. 4 hundreds 17 tens 5 ones = ____ hundreds ____ tens ____ ones

3. 1 hundred 12 tens 3 ones = ____ hundreds ____ tens ____ ones

Match each number of hundreds, tens, and ones to an equal number of hundreds, tens, and ones.

4. 8 hundreds 6 tens 4 ones   7 hundreds 10 tens 0 ones

5. 8 hundreds 2 tens 4 ones   7 hundreds 12 tens 4 ones

6. 8 hundreds 0 tens 0 ones   7 hundreds 16 tens 4 ones

Problem Solving

7. An art teacher has 400 crayons. He buys 16 more boxes. Each box has 10 crayons in it. How many crayons does the art teacher have now?

   The art teacher has _____ crayons now.

Write About It

8. Explain what happens to the number of hundreds and tens when 10 tens are regrouped as 1 hundred.

   _____

   _____

   _____

Name _____

Add: Regroup Tens as Hundreds

There are 252 adults and 354 children at a zoo. How many people are at the zoo?

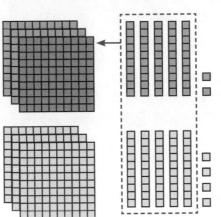

Add 252 + 354.

Look at the model. Notice that there are more than 9 tens. You will need to regroup.

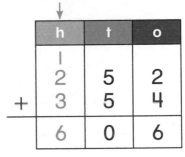

Objective
- Add three-digit numbers, regrouping tens as hundreds.

Math Words

addend
place value
regroup
ones
tens
hundreds

First add the ones.

h	t	o
2	5	2
+ 3	5	4
		6

Next add the tens. Regroup.

	h	t	o
	1		
	2	5	2
+	3	5	4
		0	6

Regroup 10 tens as 1 hundred 0 tens.

Then add the hundreds.

	h	t	o
	1		
	2	5	2
+	3	5	4
	6	0	6

There are 606 people at the zoo.

PRACTICE

Add. Regroup where needed.

1.

h	t	o
3	7	4
+	9	4

2.

h	t	o
4	5	6
+ 2	9	1

3.

h	t	o
5	4	5
+	7	4

Add. Regroup where needed.

4. 592
   +127

5. 345
   + 72

6. 482
   +363

7. 216
   + 62

8. 385
   +224

9. 523
   +467

10. 542
    + 65

11. 142
    + 86

Circle the correct sum.

12. $772 + 62 =$ _____   734   834   992

13. $168 + 340 =$ _____   408   428   508

Problem Solving

14. A bakery has 424 bagels. It has 60 more muffins than bagels. How many bagels and muffins in all?

   There are _____ bagels and muffins in all.

Write About It

15. Explain how you know when you need to regroup tens as hundreds in addition.
   Then write and solve an addition problem in which you need to regroup tens as hundreds.

   _____

   _____

   _____

Name _____

Add: Regroup Tens as Hundreds

252 + 354 = ?

There are more than 9 tens. Regroup when adding the tens.

To find the sum, you can line up the addends by place value.

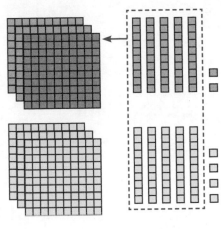

First add the ones.

h	t	o
2	5	2
+ 3	5	4
		6

Next add the tens. Regroup.

h	t	o
	1	
2	5	2
+ 3	5	4
	0	6

Regroup 10 tens as 1 hundred 0 tens.

Then add the hundreds.

h	t	o
	1	
2	5	2
+ 3	5	4
6	0	6

252 + 354 = 606

MORE PRACTICE

Add. Regroup where needed.

1.

h	t	o
3	6	2
+ 2	7	2

2.

h	t	o
1	4	3
+ 3	7	5

3.

h	t	o
4	8	3
+	4	4

Add. Regroup where needed.

1.   276
  +262
	2. 391
	  +383
		3. 137
		  + 92
			4. 823
			  + 51

Circle the correct sum.

5. $745 + 142 =$ _____   883   887   897

6. $450 + 297 =$ _____   747   737   647

Problem Solving

7. Antonio has 135 small paper clips and 170 large paper clips. How many paper clips does Antonio have in all?

Antonio has _____ paper clips in all.

Write About It

8. Jonah left out a digit when writing and solving this addition problem. What digit belongs in the box? Explain how you found the missing digit.

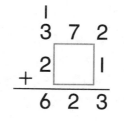

_____

_____

_____

_____

Name _____

Continue the pattern.
Write + 1, + 10, or + 100 to explain the pattern.

1. 502, 602, 702, _____   Pattern: _____

2. 116, 126, 136, _____   Pattern: _____

3. 857, 858, 859, _____   Pattern: _____

Add.

4.
$$682$$
$$+ \ 15$$

5.
$$160$$
$$+300$$

6.
$$557$$
$$+211$$

7.
$$623$$
$$+335$$

Add. Regroup where needed.

8.
$$217$$
$$+ \ 68$$

9.
$$426$$
$$+537$$

10.
$$536$$
$$+229$$

11.
$$313$$
$$+ \ 58$$

Regroup the tens. Write the new number of hundreds, tens, and ones.

12. 6 hundreds 18 tens 4 ones = ____ hundreds ____ tens ____ ones

13. 3 hundreds 15 tens 1 one = ____ hundreds ____ tens ____ one

14. 1 hundred 13 tens 7 ones = ____ hundreds ____ tens ____ ones

Add. Regroup where needed.

15. $\begin{array}{r} 395 \\ +\ 52 \\ \hline \end{array}$	16. $\begin{array}{r} 573 \\ +336 \\ \hline \end{array}$	17. $\begin{array}{r} 267 \\ +251 \\ \hline \end{array}$	18. $\begin{array}{r} 283 \\ +\ 53 \\ \hline \end{array}$
19. $\begin{array}{r} 175 \\ +383 \\ \hline \end{array}$	20. $\begin{array}{r} 628 \\ +291 \\ \hline \end{array}$	21. $\begin{array}{r} 493 \\ +451 \\ \hline \end{array}$	22. $\begin{array}{r} 736 \\ +\ 72 \\ \hline \end{array}$

Circle the correct sum.

23. $373 + 52 =$ _____   325   425   893

24. $269 + 440 =$ _____   609   619   709

Solve.

25. A petting zoo has 184 animals. If they adopt 25 more animals, how many animals will they have in all?

    _____ animals

26. There are 151 people in line for a water ride. There are 124 more people in line for a roller coaster than for the water ride. How many people in all are in line for the two rides?

    _____ people

27. Chaz has 5 hundred flats, 17 ten rods, and 2 one units. If he regroups everything he can, what number of each will Chaz have?

    _____ hundred flats _____ ten rods _____ one units

Add: Regroup Twice

There are 367 pictures displayed at an art show. Another 254 pictures are added. How many pictures are displayed now?

Add 367 + 254.

Look at the place-value model for this problem.

Objective
- Add three-digit numbers, regrouping twice.

Math Words
place value
regroup
ones
tens
hundreds

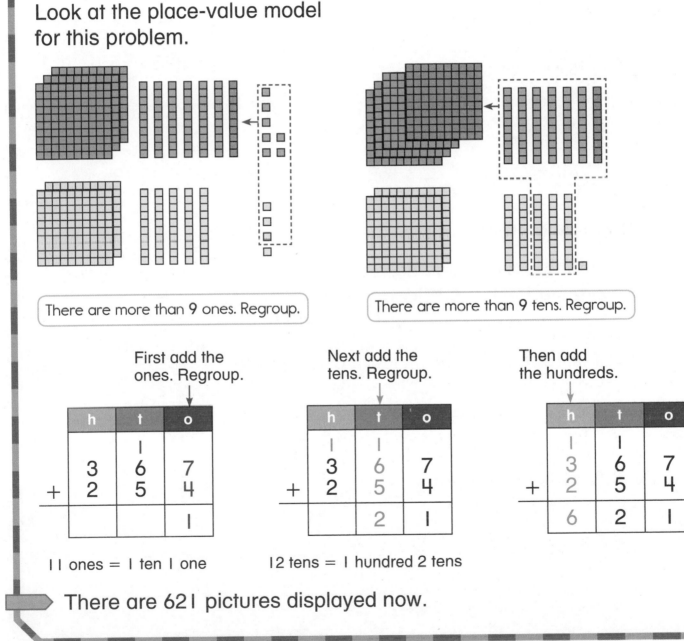

There are more than 9 ones. Regroup.

There are more than 9 tens. Regroup.

First add the ones. Regroup.

h	t	o
	1	
3	6	7
+ 2	5	4
		1

11 ones = 1 ten 1 one

Next add the tens. Regroup.

h	t	o
1	1	
3	6	7
+ 2	5	4
	2	1

12 tens = 1 hundred 2 tens

Then add the hundreds.

h	t	o
1	1	
3	6	7
+ 2	5	4
6	2	1

> There are 621 pictures displayed now.

Add. Regroup where needed.

1. $\begin{array}{r} 286 \\ +187 \\ \hline \end{array}$ 2. $\begin{array}{r} 698 \\ +209 \\ \hline \end{array}$ 3. $\begin{array}{r} 497 \\ +39 \\ \hline \end{array}$ 4. $\begin{array}{r} 768 \\ +199 \\ \hline \end{array}$

5. $\begin{array}{r} 139 \\ +374 \\ \hline \end{array}$ 6. $\begin{array}{r} 596 \\ +275 \\ \hline \end{array}$ 7. $\begin{array}{r} 372 \\ +557 \\ \hline \end{array}$ 8. $\begin{array}{r} 185 \\ +669 \\ \hline \end{array}$

Circle the correct sum.

9. $439 + 162 =$ _____   501   591   601

10. $276 + 463 =$ _____   639   739   749

Problem Solving

11. School A has 393 students. School B has
68 more students than School A. How many
students do the two schools have together?

_____ students

Write About It

12. Justin added $384 + 516$. Is he correct?
Explain why or why not.

$\begin{array}{r} {\scriptstyle 1\ 1} \\ 384 \\ +516 \\ \hline 900 \end{array}$

_____

_____

_____

Add: Regroup Twice

367 + 254 = ?

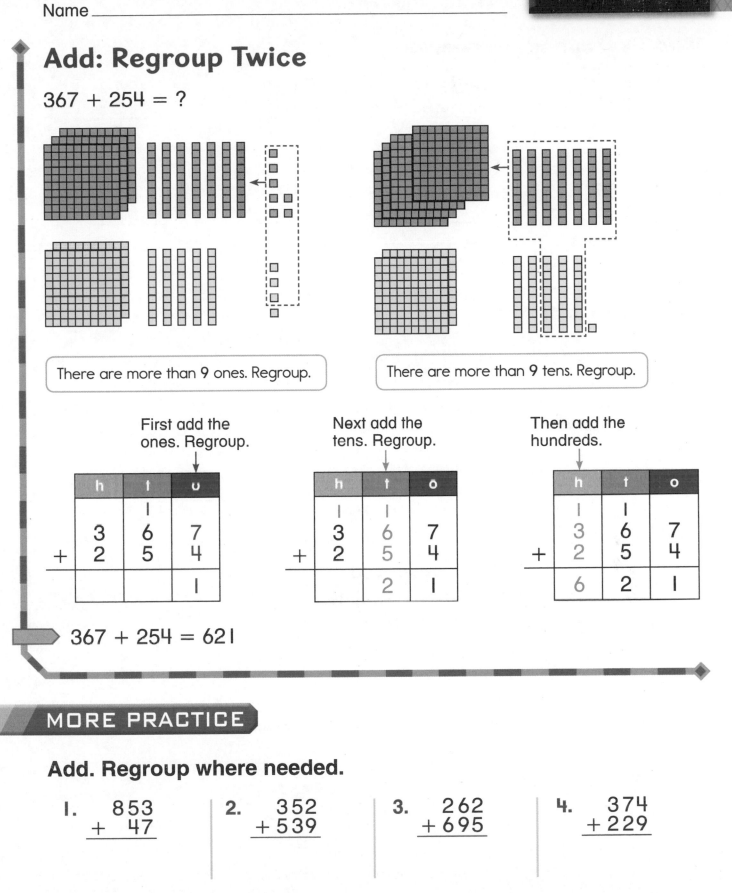

There are more than 9 ones. Regroup.

There are more than 9 tens. Regroup.

First add the ones. Regroup.

h	t	o
	I	
3	6	7
+ 2	5	4
		I

Next add the tens. Regroup.

h	t	o
I	I	
3	6	7
+ 2	5	4
	2	I

Then add the hundreds.

h	t	o
I	I	
3	6	7
+ 2	5	4
6	2	I

367 + 254 = 621

MORE PRACTICE

Add. Regroup where needed.

1. 853
    + 47

2. 352
    +539

3. 262
    +695

4. 374
    +229

Add. Regroup where needed.

1.   487
    +264
	2. 585
	    +326
		3. 158
		    +274
			4. 217
			    + 33

5.   457
    +248
	6. 288
	    +576
		7. 179
		    +625
			8. 187
			    +369

Problem Solving

9. An orchard has 478 lemon trees.
A farmer plants another 146 lemon trees.
How many lemon trees does the orchard
have now?

_____ lemon trees

Write About It

10. Explain how you know when you
need to regroup twice when adding
three-digit numbers. Then write
an addition problem in which you
need to regroup twice, and solve.

_____

_____

_____

_____

Problem Solving ⟩Read⟩⟩Plan⟩⟩Solve⟩⟩Check⟩
Make an Organized List

Objective
- Make and use an organized list for a given problem-solving situation.

Math Words
greatest
least

There are four young horses on a farm. The horses weigh 195, 203, 190, and 210 pounds. What is the total weight of the three heaviest horses?

You can make an organized list to help you solve the problem.

An organized list helps you to see information clearly.

- List the weights of the horses from greatest to least.

  210, 203, 195, 190

- Circle the three numbers you need to add.

  (210), (203), (195), 190

- Add the first two numbers.

$$\begin{array}{r} 210 \\ +203 \\ \hline 413 \end{array}$$

- Then add the third number to the sum. Regroup where needed.

$$\begin{array}{r} 1 \\ 413 \\ +195 \\ \hline 608 \end{array}$$

⟩ The total weight of the three heaviest horses is 608 pounds.

Read and solve each problem. You can make an organized list to help you solve some of the problems.

1. Ryan's house number is a three-digit number. It has the digits 6, 3, and 8 in it, but he does not remember the order. What could Ryan's house number be? List all the possible numbers.

   _____

2. Sophia drew 4 shapes in a row. She drew a square last. She drew a circle next to a triangle. The circle is not next to the square. Then Sophia drew a star next to the circle. The triangle is not first in line. Draw and order Sophia's shapes.

Write About It

3. Sam checks out four books from the library. The books have 343, 194, 426, and 418 pages. Sam reads the book with the least number of pages and the book with the greatest number of pages. How many pages does he read in all? Explain how you solved the problem.

   _____

   _____

   _____

   _____

Problem Solving
Make an Organized List

Four young horses live on a farm.
The horses weigh 195, 203, 190, and
210 pounds. What is the total weight
of the three heaviest horses?

You can make an organized list to help you
solve the problem.

An organized list helps you to see
information clearly.

- List the weights from greatest to least.

  210, 203, 195, 190

- Circle the three numbers you need to add.

  (210), (203), (195), 190

- Add the first two numbers.

$$\begin{array}{r} 210 \\ +203 \\ \hline 413 \end{array}$$

- Then add the third number to the sum.

$$\begin{array}{r} 1 \\ 413 \\ +195 \\ \hline 608 \end{array}$$

  10 tens = 1 hundred 0 tens

▷ The total weight of the three heaviest horses
is 608 pounds.

Read and solve each problem. You can make an organized list to help you solve.

1. Andrew's family drove 228, 194, 281, and 252 miles on four different days of their vacation. What is the total number of miles for the two days they drove the farthest?

   List the miles driven from greatest to least. Circle the numbers you need to add to solve the problem.

   _____

   Andrew's family drove _____ miles on the two days they drove the farthest.

2. Jada keeps track of how many minutes she practices the piano each week. Her times for the last four weeks are 155, 120, 95, and 160 minutes. What is the total number of minutes for the three weeks she practiced the least?

   List the numbers of minutes from least to greatest:

   _____

   Jada practiced _____ minutes during the three weeks she practiced the least.

3. Tyler has 81 horses on his farm. He put some in the barn and 15 in trucks. There are still 37 horses outside. How many horses did Tyler put in the barn?

   Tyler put _____ horses in the barn.

HOMEWORK

Read and solve each problem. You can make an organized list to help you solve.

1. A theater sold 324 tickets on Monday, 297 tickets on Tuesday, 255 on Wednesday, and 402 on Thursday. How many tickets did the theater sell on the two days with the lowest sales?

   List the numbers of tickets from least to greatest:

   _____

   The theater sold _____ tickets on the two days with the lowest sales.

2. An artist needs a piece of ribbon that is 67 centimeters long. She has a piece that is 85 centimeters long, but cuts off and uses 17 centimeters. Is the remaining ribbon longer or shorter than 67 centimeters?

   The remaining ribbon is _____ than 67 centimeters.

3. A snack shop sells 205 granola bars, 240 bottles of flavored water, 232 sandwiches, and 211 bags of popcorn. What is the total number of items sold for the three most popular items?

   List the numbers of items from greatest to least:

   _____

   The snack shop sold _____ of the three most popular items.

4. There are 96 people in the park. 37 people leave the park. Then 115 more people come. How many people are in the park now?

There are _____ people in the park now.

---

5. A librarian is putting 87 books in boxes for the book sale. He puts 10 books in each box. How many boxes will he fill, and how many extra books will he have?

The librarian will fill ____ boxes and have

____ extra books.

---

6. Four students are in line. Maria is next to Sarah. Grace is not last. Kim is first. Maria is third. What is the order of the students, from first to last?

_____

Write About It

7. Juan, Darren, and Paul are playing a computer game. Juan scores 168 points. Darren scores 139 points more than Juan. Paul scores 298 points. What is the total number of points for the two highest scores? Explain how you solved the problem.

_____

_____

_____

_____

Use Properties to Add

Objective
■ Use strategies based on properties of operations to add three-digit numbers.

Math Words
break apart
addend
group

A craft store sold 264 purple buttons and 153 yellow buttons. How many buttons did the craft store sell in all?

You can break apart addends to make addition easier. You can group and add the addends in any order.

- Break apart the addends into hundreds, tens, and ones.

- Group the hundreds, tens, and ones.

- Add the hundreds, tens, and ones.

- Regroup where needed.

- Add to find the sum.

The craft store sold 417 buttons in all.

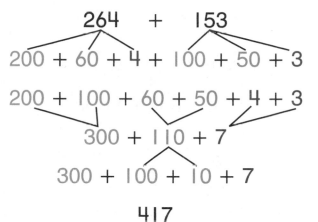

$$264 + 153$$
$$200 + 60 + 4 + 100 + 50 + 3$$
$$200 + 100 + 60 + 50 + 4 + 3$$
$$300 + 110 + 7$$
$$300 + 100 + 10 + 7$$
$$417$$

PRACTICE

Find the missing numbers. Break apart to add.

1.
$$427 + 346$$
$$400 + 20 + 7 + \underline{} + 40 + 6$$
$$400 + 300 + 20 + 40 + 7 + 6$$
$$\underline{} + \underline{} + \underline{}$$
$$700 + 60 + 10 + \underline{}$$

$$\underline{}$$

Find the missing numbers.
Break apart to add.

2.

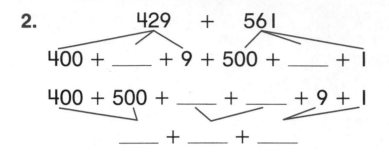

429 + 561

400 + ___ + 9 + 500 + ___ + 1

400 + 500 + ___ + ___ + 9 + 1

___ + ___ + ___

___

Problem Solving

3. There are 224 people swimming and 258 people boating at a beach. How many people are at the beach in all? Break apart the addends to solve.

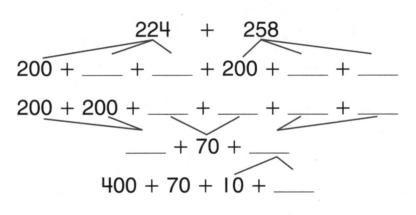

224 + 258

200 + ___ + ___ + 200 + ___ + ___

200 + 200 + ___ + ___ + ___ + ___

___ + 70 + ___

400 + 70 + 10 + ___

___

There are _____ people at the beach in all.

Write About It

4. Why is adding 328 + 641 the same as adding 300 + 600 + 20 + 40 + 8 + 1?

_____

_____

_____

_____

Using Properties to Add

264 + 153 = ?

You can break apart and add addends in any order.

- Break apart the addends.

- Group the hundreds, tens, and ones.

- Add the sums.

- Regroup where needed.

- Add to find the sum.

264 + 153 = 417

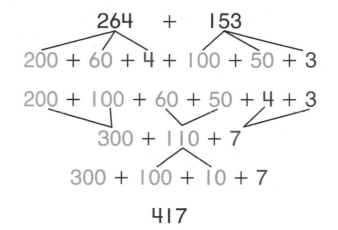

$$264 \quad + \quad 153$$
$$200 + 60 + 4 + 100 + 50 + 3$$
$$200 + 100 + 60 + 50 + 4 + 3$$
$$300 + 110 + 7$$
$$300 + 100 + 10 + 7$$
$$417$$

MORE PRACTICE

Find the missing numbers.
Break apart to add.

1. 272 + 395 = ?

$$272 \quad + \quad 395$$
$$200 + 70 + 2 + 300 + 90 + \underline{\quad}$$
$$200 + 300 + 70 + 90 + 2 + \underline{\quad}$$
$$\underline{\quad} + 160 + \underline{\quad}$$
$$500 + 100 + \underline{\quad} + 7$$

$$\underline{\quad}$$

272 + 395 = _____

Find the missing numbers. Break apart to add.

1. 263 + 242 = ?

263 + 242

200 + ___ + 3 + 200 + ___ + 2

200 + 200 + ___ + ___ + 3 + 2

___ + ___ + ___

___

Problem Solving

2. A tile floor has 434 blue tiles and 512 gray tiles. How many tiles are there in all? Break apart the numbers to solve.

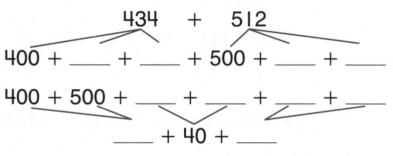

434 + 512

400 + ___ + ___ + 500 + ___ + ___

400 + 500 + ___ + ___ + ___ + ___

___ + 40 + ___

___

There are _____ tiles in all.

Write About It

3. Ruby and Kelly broke apart addends to find 428 + 351.
   Ruby wrote 400 + 20 + 8 + 300 + 50 + 1.
   Kelly wrote 400 + 300 + 20 + 50 + 8 + 1.
   Who will get the correct sum? Explain.

_____

_____

_____

_____

Name _____

Continue the pattern. Write + 1, + 10, or + 100 to explain the pattern.

1. 425, 435, 445, _____   Pattern: _____

2. 361, 461, 561, _____   Pattern: _____

3. 787, 788, 789, _____   Pattern: _____

Add. Regroup where needed.

4.
$$\begin{array}{r} 1 \\ 337 \\ +47 \\ \hline \end{array}$$

5.
$$\begin{array}{r} 1 \\ 506 \\ +245 \\ \hline \end{array}$$

6.
$$\begin{array}{r} 1 \\ 464 \\ +219 \\ \hline \end{array}$$

7.
$$\begin{array}{r} 1 \\ 806 \\ +88 \\ \hline \end{array}$$

Regroup the tens. Write the new number of hundreds, tens, and ones.

8. 5 hundreds 11 tens 9 ones = _____ hundreds _____ ten _____ ones

9. 7 hundreds 18 tens 6 ones = _____ hundreds _____ tens _____ ones

Add. Regroup where needed.

10.
$$\begin{array}{r} 1 \\ 485 \\ +41 \\ \hline \end{array}$$

11.
$$\begin{array}{r} 1 \\ 543 \\ +264 \\ \hline \end{array}$$

12.
$$\begin{array}{r} 1 \\ 163 \\ +275 \\ \hline \end{array}$$

13.
$$\begin{array}{r} 1 \\ 373 \\ +451 \\ \hline \end{array}$$

14.
$$\begin{array}{r} 11 \\ 557 \\ +85 \\ \hline \end{array}$$

15.
$$\begin{array}{r} 11 \\ 295 \\ +146 \\ \hline \end{array}$$

16.
$$\begin{array}{r} 11 \\ 369 \\ +388 \\ \hline \end{array}$$

17.
$$\begin{array}{r} 11 \\ 757 \\ +43 \\ \hline \end{array}$$

Circle the correct sums.

18.   **A.**
$$\overset{\text{1 1}}{375} \atop +52 \over 437$$

B.
$$\overset{\text{1 1}}{169} \atop +254 \over 423$$

C.
$$\overset{\text{1 1}}{479} \atop +375 \over 854$$

Find the missing numbers. Break apart to add.

19.

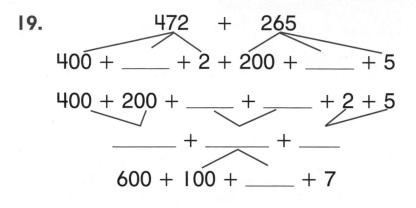

472 + 265

400 + ____ + 2 + 200 + ____ + 5

400 + 200 + ____ + ____ + 2 + 5

____ + ____ + ____

600 + 100 + ____ + 7

____

Solve.

20. A farm stand sells 283 plums. It sells 57 more peaches than plums. How many plums and peaches does the farm stand sell in all?

_____ plums and peaches

21. A school recycled 97 bottles on Monday, 204 bottles on Tuesday, and 166 bottles on Wednesday. It recycled 242 bottles on Thursday and 145 bottles on Friday. How many bottles did the school recycle in all on its 3 best days?

List the numbers of bottles from greatest to least:

_____

The school recycled _____ bottles in all on its 3 best days.

Name _____

The table shows information about the lengths of some airplane wingspans.

Wingspan (in feet)	
Plane A	197
Plane B	243
Plane C	171

1. What is the combined wingspan of the two smallest planes? Explain how you solved the problem.

_____

_____

_____

2. Suppose you are hired to design an airport terminal. The terminal has 7 gates next to each other. There is room for 1 plane at each gate. Research the wingspans of 4 different-sized planes. Record the lengths in the table. Then find the total length needed for the terminal, based on the wingspans of your planes. Remember that different planes need to use the gates at different times. Also remember to add extra room between the gates for safety and for the jet ways to connect to the planes!

Wingspan (in feet)	
Plane A	
Plane B	
Plane C	
Plane D	

Length of airport terminal:

_____ feet

Determine the best answer for each problem.

1. Add.

   $5 + 6 + 4 =$ _____

2. Use mental math to add.

   $170 + 20 =$ _____

3. Which tool and units would be **best** to use to measure the length of a real truck?

   A. ruler, inches
   B. yardstick, feet
   C. ruler, feet

4. Compare the numbers.
   793 (?) 796

   A. $>$
   B. $<$
   C. $=$

5. Write 492 in expanded form.

   _____ + _____ + _____

6. Subtract.

   $$\begin{array}{r} 67 \\ -38 \\ \hline \end{array}$$

7. Add.

   $$\begin{array}{r} 453 \\ +178 \\ \hline \end{array}$$

8. Which two additions have a sum greater than 73?

   A. $40 + 25$
   B. $38 + 36$
   C. $57 + 20$

9. How many hundreds are in 487?

   A. 4 hundreds
   B. 7 hundreds
   C. 8 hundreds

10. Which is equal to 509?

   A. $5 + 0 + 9$
   B. $500 + 9$
   C. $50 + 9$

Subtraction: Three-Digit Numbers

Some engineers study ways to save energy. They help make the machines and tools in homes use less energy.

Types of Technology

♦ There are new types of lightbulbs that use less energy.

♦ New technology in machines helps save energy.

More Information, Better Choices

♦ Some appliances come with energy labels that tell how much energy they use.

♦ Do you think saving energy can save you money, too?

Dear Family,

In this chapter, we will be subtracting three-digit numbers.

Here are the key Math Words for this chapter:

count back   tens

difference   hundreds

regroup   place value

ones

Terms such as *tens*, *hundreds*, and *difference* are not new to students. Some Math Words are repeated, as they set a foundation for building students' understanding of and fluency with subtraction. Use the glossary to find the definition of each word and help your child make flash cards to study each day throughout the chapter.

During this chapter, we will also be making STEAM (Science, Technology, Engineering, the Arts, and Mathematics) connections about appliances and energy efficiency.

Keep Your Skills Sharp

Here is a **Keep Your Skills Sharp** activity to do at home.

Play number riddles with your child. One player thinks of a three-digit number and gives clues to the other player. For example, "My number has 7 in the hundreds place, a tens digit with a value of 40, and a ones digit 5 less than the hundreds digit. What is my number?" (742). Switch roles and play again.

Name _____

Mental Math: Subtract 1, 10, or 100

Objective
- Use mental math to subtract 1, 10, or 100.

Math Word
count back

Ryan, Carlos, and Ian play a game. Each player starts with 350 points. During the game, Ryan loses 1 point, Carlos loses 10 points, and Ian loses 100 points. How many points does each player have at the end of the game?

You can count back to subtract mentally.

$350 - 1 = ?$	$350 - 10 = ?$	$350 - 100 = ?$
Count back 1.	Count back 10.	Count back 100.
350, 349	350, 340	350, 250
$350 - 1 = 349$	$350 - 10 = 340$	$350 - 100 = 250$

At the end of the game, Ryan has 349 points, Carlos has 340 points, and Ian has 250 points.

PRACTICE

Write the number 1 less than each.

1. ____, 530 | 2. ____, 318 | 3. ____, 800 | 4. ____, 635

Write the number 10 less than each.

5. ____, 138 | 6. ____, 400 | 7. ____, 215 | 8. ____, 150

Write the number 100 less than each.

9. ____, 900 | 10. ____, 474 | 11. ____, 749 | 12. ____, 161

Continue the pattern. Write − 1, − 10, or − 100 to explain the pattern.

13. 627, 626, 625, _____   Pattern: _____

14. 806, 706, 606, _____   Pattern: _____

15. 754, 744, 734, _____   Pattern: _____

> Look for the change in the hundreds place when subtracting 100. Look for similar changes when subtracting 10 and 1.

Subtract.

16. $315 − 10 =$ _____

17. $346 − 1 =$ _____

Problem Solving

18. Amanda reads 300 pages of a book.
    Michelle reads 10 fewer pages than Amanda.
    Evelyn reads 1 fewer page than Michelle.
    How many pages does Evelyn read?

    Evelyn reads _____ pages.

Write About It

19. Without subtracting, tell whether $857 − 10$ or $857 − 100$ is less. Explain how you know.

    _____

    _____

    _____

LESSON 9-1

Name _____

Mental Math: Subtract 1, 10, or 100

You can count back mentally to subtract.

$350 - 1 = ?$	$350 - 10 = ?$	$350 - 100 = ?$
Count back 1.	Count back 10.	Count back 100.
350, 349	350, 340	350, 250
$350 - 1 = 349$	$350 - 10 = 340$	$350 - 100 = 250$

MORE PRACTICE

Write the number 1 less than each.

1. ____, 850

2. ____, 635

3. ____, 515

4. ____, 700

Write the number 10 less than each.

5. ____, 212

6. ____, 832

7. ____, 600

8. ____, 513

Write the number 100 less than each.

9. ____, 876

10. ____, 251

11. ____, 815

12. ____, 499

Subtract.

13. $720 - 1 =$ ____

14. $312 - 100 =$ ____

15. $675 - 10 =$ ____

16. $237 - 10 =$ ____

17. $299 - 100 =$ ____

18. $511 - 1 =$ ____

Subtract.

1. 320 – 1 = _____

2. 145 – 100 = _____

3. 538 – 10 = _____

4. 600 – 1 = _____

Continue the pattern. Write – 1, – 10, or – 100 to explain the pattern.

5. 438, 338, 238, _____   Pattern: _____

6. 841, 840, 839, _____   Pattern: _____

Problem Solving

7. Oscar is 20 years old. His brother Sam is 1 year younger, and his cousin is 10 years younger than Sam. How old is Oscar's cousin?

   Oscar's cousin is _____ years old.

Write About It

8. How can you decide whether a list of numbers has a – 100, – 10, or – 1 pattern?

   _____

   _____

   _____

   _____

   _____

Name _____

Subtract Hundreds, Tens, and Ones

Objective
- Subtract three-digit numbers without regrouping.

Math Words
difference
place value
ones
tens
hundreds

A theater has 475 seats. If 352 seats are filled, how many seats are empty?

Look at the place-value model for this problem.

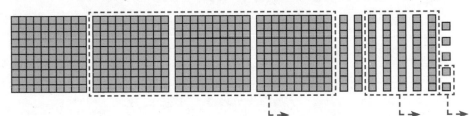

Subtract 475 − 352 to find the difference.

Line up the numbers by place value.

First subtract the ones.

h	t	o
4	7	5
− 3	5	2
		3

Next subtract the tens.

h	t	o
4	7	5
− 3	5	2
	2	3

Then subtract the hundreds.

h	t	o
4	7	5
− 3	5	2
1	2	3

There are 123 empty seats in the theater.

PRACTICE

Subtract. Start with the ones.

1.

h	t	o
2	5	8
− 2	2	6

2.

h	t	o
5	8	9
−	3	5

3.

h	t	o
6	6	7
− 3	6	4

Subtract.

4. $\begin{array}{r} 906 \\ -405 \\ \hline \end{array}$

5. $\begin{array}{r} 849 \\ -136 \\ \hline \end{array}$

6. $\begin{array}{r} 667 \\ -\ 46 \\ \hline \end{array}$

7. $\begin{array}{r} 478 \\ -158 \\ \hline \end{array}$

Line up the numbers by place value and subtract.

8. 344 − 34 = _____

9. 695 − 141 = _____

10. 765 − 311 = _____

11. 445 − 23 = _____

Problem Solving

12. Ella and Ruby are both reading a book that has 196 pages. Ella has read 24 pages. Ruby has read 106 pages. How many pages does each girl have left to read? Use the place-value charts to show your work.

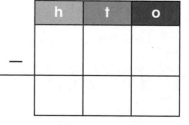

    Ella has _____ pages left to read.

    Ruby has _____ pages left to read.

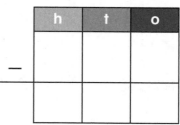

Write About It

13. Alex subtracted 675 − 54. Explain the mistake he made. Then write the correct difference.

$\begin{array}{r} 675 \\ -\ 54 \\ \hline 135 \end{array}$

_____

_____

_____

LESSON 9-2

Name _____

Subtract Hundreds, Tens, and Ones

475 − 352 = ?

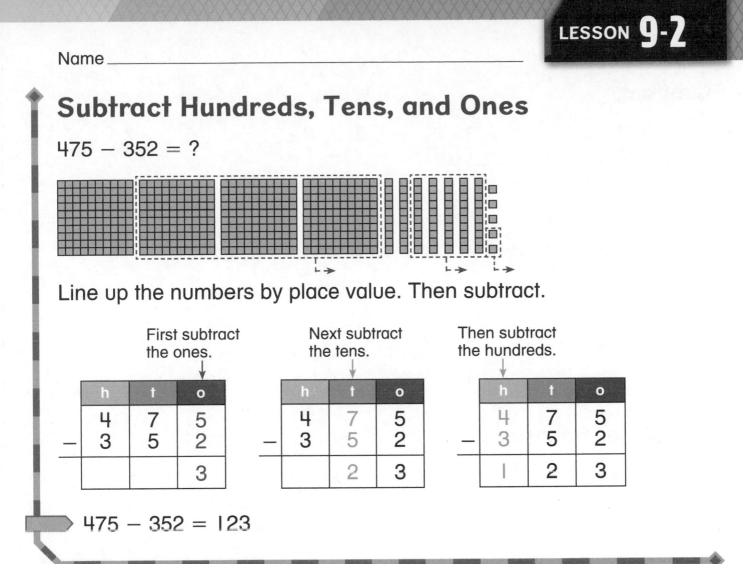

Line up the numbers by place value. Then subtract.

First subtract the ones.

h	t	o
4	7	5
− 3	5	2
		3

Next subtract the tens.

h	t	o
4	7	5
− 3	5	2
	2	3

Then subtract the hundreds.

h	t	o
4	7	5
− 3	5	2
1	2	3

475 − 352 = 123

MORE PRACTICE

Subtract. Start with the ones.

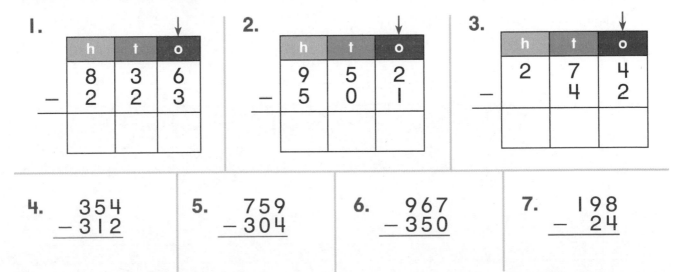

1.

h	t	o
8	3	6
− 2	2	3

2.

h	t	o
9	5	2
− 5	0	1

3.

h	t	o
2	7	4
−	4	2

4.   354
   − 3 1 2

5.   759
   − 304

6.   967
   − 350

7.   198
   − 24

Subtract.

1. $\begin{array}{r} 698 \\ -631 \\ \hline \end{array}$

2. $\begin{array}{r} 397 \\ -123 \\ \hline \end{array}$

3. $\begin{array}{r} 423 \\ -103 \\ \hline \end{array}$

4. $\begin{array}{r} 879 \\ -327 \\ \hline \end{array}$

Line up the numbers by place value and subtract.

5. $256 - 42 \ = \ \underline{\hspace{1cm}}$

6. $738 - 136 \ = \ \underline{\hspace{1cm}}$

7. $575 - 341 \ = \ \underline{\hspace{1cm}}$

8. $966 - 345 \ = \ \underline{\hspace{1cm}}$

Problem Solving

9. Hector has 324 marbles in his collection.
   He gives 102 marbles to his brother. How many
   marbles are in Hector's collection now?

   Hector has _____ marbles now.

Write About It

10. Kelsey subtracted $758 - 124$.
    First she subtracted the ones: $8 - 4 = 4$
    Then she subtracted the tens: $5 - 2 = 3$
    Finally, she subtracted the hundreds: $7 - 1 = 6$

    She says the answer is 436. Is Kelsey correct? Explain.

    _____

    _____

    _____

Name _____

Subtract: Regroup Tens as Ones

Objective
■ Subtract three-digit numbers, regrouping tens as ones.

Math Words
difference
place value
regroup
ones
tens
hundreds

There are 465 people on a train. Then 256 people get off. How many people are left on the train?

Subtract 465 − 256 to find the difference.

Look at the place-value models for this problem.

There are not enough ones to subtract 6 ones from 5 ones. Regroup 1 ten as 10 ones.

After regrouping, there are enough ones to subtract 6 ones from 15 ones.

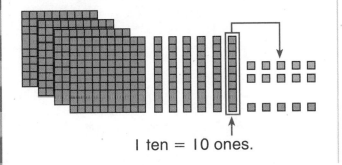

1 ten = 10 ones.

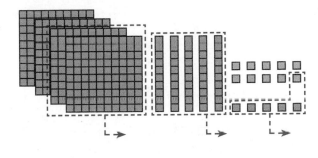

Line up the numbers by place value. Subtract.

First regroup. Then subtract the ones.

Next subtract the tens.

Then subtract the hundreds.

Regroup 6 tens 5 ones as 5 tens 15 ones.

h	t	o
	5	15
4	6̶	5̶
− 2	5	6
		9

h	t	o
	5	15
4	6̶	5̶
− 2	5	6
	0	9

h	t	o
	5	15
4	6̶	5̶
− 2	5	6
2	0	9

▷ There are 209 people left on the train.

Subtract. Regroup where needed.

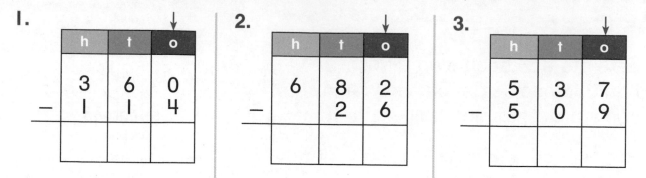

1.

h	t	o
3	6	0
− 1	1	4

2.

h	t	o
6	8	2
−	2	6

3.

h	t	o
5	3	7
− 5	0	9

Subtract. Regroup where needed.

4.
```
  2 6 3
−   4 4
```

5.
```
  7 8 1
− 3 4 5
```

6.
```
  5 7 5
− 3 3 7
```

7.
```
  9 1 0
− 3 0 5
```

Problem Solving

8. A flower shop has 172 roses. 58 of the roses are pink. The other roses are red. How many red roses are there?

_____ red roses

Write About It

9. Nora subtracted 526 − 319. Is she correct? Explain. Then write the correct difference.

```
  5 2 6
− 3 1 9
  2 1 3
```

Name_____

Subtract: Regroup Tens as Ones

465 − 256 = ?

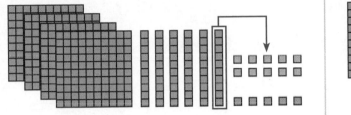

There are not enough ones.
Regroup 1 ten as 10 ones.

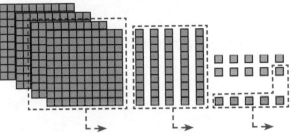

After regrouping, you can
subtract 6 ones from 15 ones.

Find the difference. Line up the numbers by place value.

Regroup 6 tens
5 ones as
5 tens 15 ones.

Regroup. Subtract ones. ↓

h	t	o
	5	15
4	6̶	5̶
− 2	5	6
		9

Subtract tens. ↓

h	t	o
	5	15
4	6̶	5̶
− 2	5	6
	0	9

Subtract hundreds. ↓

h	t	o
	5	15
4	6̶	5̶
− 2	5	6
2	0	9

465 − 256 = 209

MORE PRACTICE

Subtract. Regroup where needed.

1.

h	t	o ↓
5	8	3
−	5	6

2.

h	t	o ↓
1	4	1
− 1	2	9

3.

h	t	o ↓
6	3	0
− 4	0	2

Subtract. Regroup where needed.

1.
```
  7 9 6
- 5 7 7
```

2.
```
  8 3 2
- 1 2 5
```

3.
```
  4 8 3
- 2 0 4
```

4.
```
  8 6 0
- 7 0 2
```

Line up the numbers by place value and subtract.

5. $280 - 237 =$ _____

6. $691 - 343 =$ _____

7. $422 - 113 =$ _____

8. $553 - 126 =$ _____

Problem Solving

9. There are 325 tickets for a play. The box office sells 218 tickets. How many tickets are left?

There are _____ tickets left.

Write About It

10. Tyler subtracted $352 - 129$. Is he correct? Explain.

```
    4 10
  3 5̸ 2̸
- 1 2 9
  2 2 1
```

_____

_____

_____

_____

_____

Regroup Hundreds as Tens Using Models

Objective
▪ Use models to regroup hundreds as tens.

Math Words
regroup
model
ones
tens
hundreds

A ticket seller has 4 rolls of 100 tickets, 2 strips of 10 tickets, and 7 single tickets. She breaks up one roll of 100 tickets to make more strips of 10. How many tickets of each type are there now?

Model 4 hundreds, 2 tens, and 7 ones.

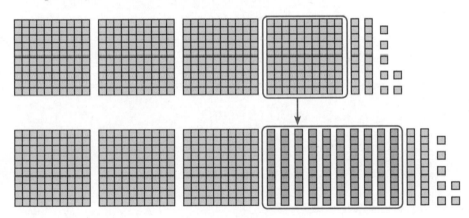

Regroup 1 hundred as tens.

1 hundred = 10 tens

Count the new number of hundreds, tens, and ones

3 hundreds   12 tens   7 ones

4 hundreds 2 tens 7 ones = 3 hundreds 12 tens 7 ones.

▷ There are 3 rolls of 100 tickets, 12 strips of 10 tickets, and 7 single tickets.

**Use models to regroup I hundred as I0 tens.
Write the new number of hundreds, tens, and ones.**

1.

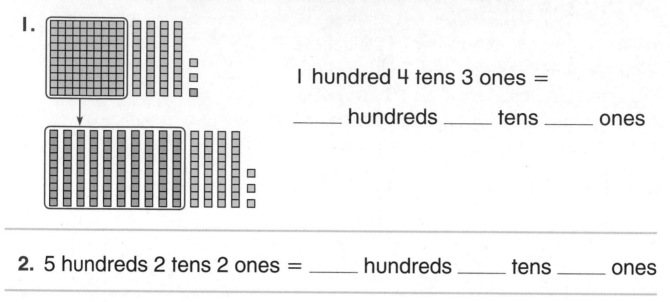

I hundred 4 tens 3 ones =

_____ hundreds _____ tens _____ ones

2. 5 hundreds 2 tens 2 ones = _____ hundreds _____ tens _____ ones

3. 2 hundreds 3 tens 8 ones = _____ hundred _____ tens _____ ones

Problem Solving

4. Evan is thinking of a number. If he regroups
   I hundred as I0 tens, his number would have
   6 hundreds, I8 tens, and I one.
   What number is Evan thinking of?

   Evan is thinking of the number _____.

Write About It

5. Explain what happens to the number of hundreds, tens,
   and ones when I hundred is regrouped as I0 tens.

   _____

   _____

   _____

Regroup Hundreds as Tens Using Models

How can you regroup 4 hundreds, 2 tens, and 7 ones? You can regroup 1 hundred as 10 tens.

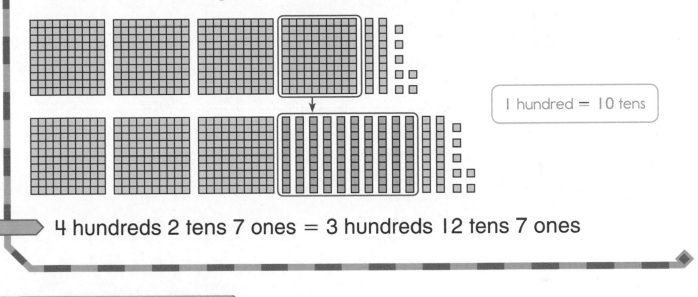

I hundred = 10 tens

➤ 4 hundreds 2 tens 7 ones = 3 hundreds 12 tens 7 ones

MORE PRACTICE

Regroup 1 hundred as 10 tens. Write the new number of hundreds, tens, and ones.

1. 3 hundreds 5 tens 7 ones = _____ hundreds _____ tens _____ ones

2. 1 hundred 3 tens 5 ones = _____ hundreds _____ tens _____ ones

3. 4 hundreds 6 tens 4 ones = _____ hundreds _____ tens _____ ones

Match each number of hundreds, tens, and ones to the number that has the same value.

4. 8 hundreds 17 tens 6 ones   **A.** 906

5. 8 hundreds 14 tens 6 ones   **B.** 946

6. 8 hundreds 10 tens 6 ones   **C.** 976

Regroup 1 hundred as 10 tens. Write the new number of hundreds, tens, and ones.

1. 4 hundreds 8 tens 2 ones = _____ hundreds _____ tens _____ ones

2. 1 hundred 2 tens 3 ones = _____ hundreds _____ tens _____ ones

3. 9 hundreds 3 tens 0 ones = _____ hundreds _____ tens _____ ones

Match each number of hundreds, tens, and ones to an equivalent number of hundreds, tens, and ones.

4. 3 hundreds 10 tens 5 ones   A. 4 hundreds 5 tens 0 ones

5. 3 hundreds 15 tens 0 ones   B. 4 hundreds 0 tens 5 ones

6. 3 hundreds 15 tens 5 ones   C. 4 hundreds 5 tens 5 ones

Problem Solving

7. Bianca is thinking of a number. If she regroups 1 hundred as 10 tens, her number would have 0 hundreds, 15 tens, and 6 ones. What number is Bianca thinking of?

   Bianca is thinking of the number _____.

Write About It

8. What happens to the value of a three-digit number when you regroup 1 hundred as 10 tens? Explain.

   _____

   _____

   _____

Name _____

Subtract: Regroup Hundreds as Tens

A school has 325 students. 143 of the students ride the bus. How many of the students do not ride the bus?

Subtract 325 − 143 to find the difference.

Line up the numbers by place value to subtract.

Regroup 1 hundred as 10 tens.

Objective
▪ Subtract three-digit numbers, regrouping hundreds as tens.

Math Words
place value
regroup
ones
tens
hundreds

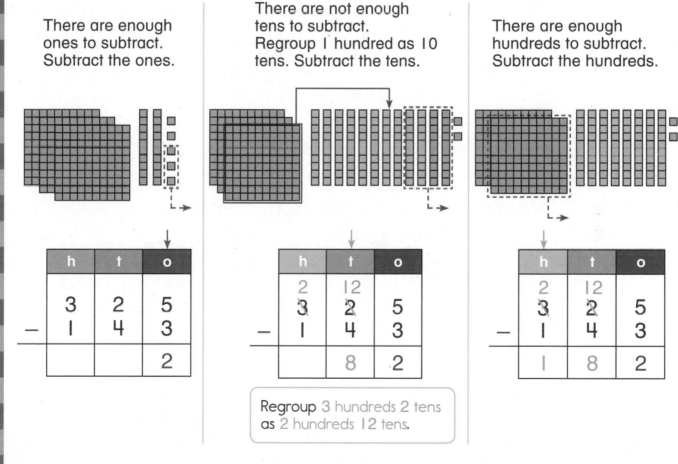

There are enough ones to subtract. Subtract the ones.

There are not enough tens to subtract. Regroup 1 hundred as 10 tens. Subtract the tens.

There are enough hundreds to subtract. Subtract the hundreds.

h	t	o
3	2	5
− 1	4	3
		2

h	t	o
2	12	
3	2	5
− 1	4	3
	8	2

Regroup 3 hundreds 2 tens as 2 hundreds 12 tens.

h	t	o
2	12	
3	2	5
− 1	4	3
1	8	2

182 students do not ride the bus.

Subtract. Regroup where needed.

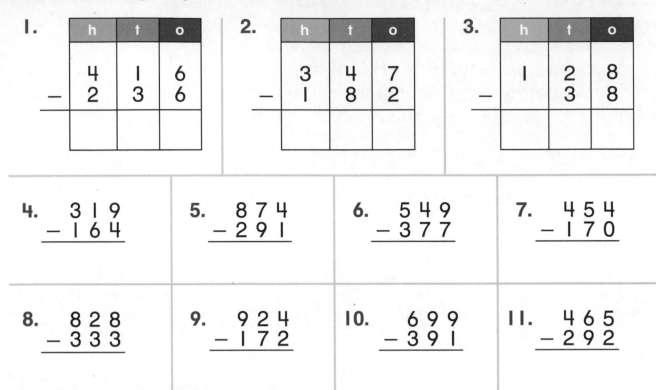

1.

h	t	o
4	1	6
− 2	3	6

2.

h	t	o
3	4	7
− 1	8	2

3.

h	t	o
1	2	8
−	3	8

4.
```
  3 1 9
− 1 6 4
```

5.
```
  8 7 4
− 2 9 1
```

6.
```
  5 4 9
− 3 7 7
```

7.
```
  4 5 4
− 1 7 0
```

8.
```
  8 2 8
− 3 3 3
```

9.
```
  9 2 4
− 1 7 2
```

10.
```
  6 9 9
− 3 9 1
```

11.
```
  4 6 5
− 2 9 2
```

Problem Solving

12. A bakery makes 358 muffins. It sells 166 muffins in the morning. How many muffins are left?

_____ muffins are left.

Write About It

13. Explain how regrouping hundreds as tens is like regrouping tens as ones.

_____

_____

_____

_____

Subtract: Regroup Hundreds as Tens

325 − 143 = ?

Line up the numbers by place value to subtract.

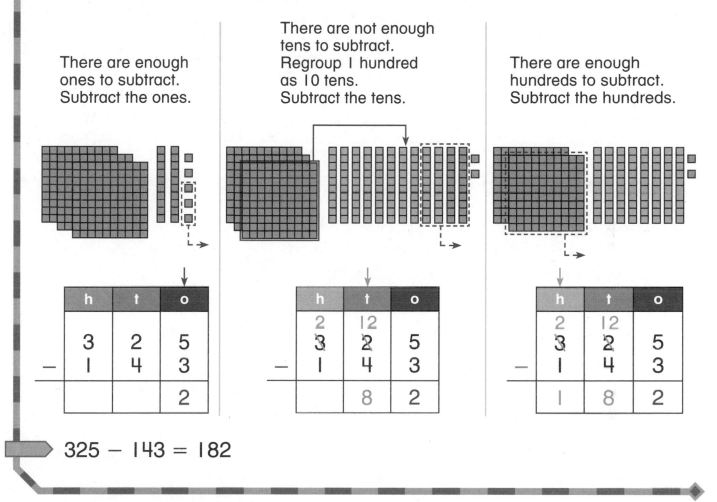

There are enough ones to subtract. Subtract the ones.

h	t	o
3	2	5
− 1	4	3
		2

There are not enough tens to subtract. Regroup 1 hundred as 10 tens. Subtract the tens.

h	t	o
2/3	12/2	5
− 1	4	3
	8	2

There are enough hundreds to subtract. Subtract the hundreds.

h	t	o
2/3	12/2	5
− 1	4	3
1	8	2

▷ 325 − 143 = 182

MORE PRACTICE

Subtract. Regroup where needed.

1.

h	t	o
7	3	5
− 3	6	2

2.

h	t	o
9	7	1
− 5	9	0

3.

h	t	o
4	1	9
−	5	4

Subtract. Regroup where needed.

1. $\begin{array}{r} 756 \\ -681 \\ \hline \end{array}$

2. $\begin{array}{r} 469 \\ -146 \\ \hline \end{array}$

3. $\begin{array}{r} 728 \\ -56 \\ \hline \end{array}$

4. $\begin{array}{r} 635 \\ -584 \\ \hline \end{array}$

Line up the numbers by place value and subtract.

5. $749 - 473 =$ _____

6. $657 - 62 =$ _____

Problem Solving

7. Students collected 760 cans for a food drive.
The goal is to collect 915 cans of food.
How many more cans are needed to reach
the goal?

_____ more cans are needed.

Write About It

8. Jacob subtracted $426 - 172$.
Is he correct? Explain why or why not.
Then write the correct difference if needed.

$\begin{array}{r} \overset{12}{4}\overset{}{\cancel{2}}6 \\ -172 \\ \hline 354 \end{array}$

_____

_____

_____

_____

_____

Continue the pattern. Write −1, −10, or −100 to explain the pattern.

1. 809, 709, 609, _____   Pattern: _____

2. 544, 534, 524, _____   Pattern: _____

3. 632, 631, 630, _____   Pattern: _____

Subtract.

4.
```
  5 3 8
−   1 7
```

5.
```
  7 0 5
− 3 0 1
```

6.
```
  4 8 9
− 2 7 5
```

7.
```
  1 9 6
−   7 3
```

Subtract. Regroup where needed.

8.
```
  6 5 1
−   4 7
```

9.
```
  5 3 6
−   2 6
```

10.
```
  8 8 1
− 3 4 5
```

11.
```
  3 5 2
− 1 3 8
```

Regroup 1 hundred as 10 tens. Write the new number of hundreds, tens, and ones.

12. 6 hundreds 5 tens 0 ones = _____ hundreds _____ tens _____ ones

13. 1 hundred 0 tens 8 ones = _____ hundreds _____ tens _____ ones

14. 8 hundreds 1 ten 2 ones = _____ hundreds _____ tens _____ ones

Subtract. Regroup where needed.

15.
```
  7 3 1
– 1 8 0
```

16.
```
  5 6 7
– 3 1 5
```

17.
```
  8 1 6
– 1 0 9
```

18.
```
  5 1 2
–   9 1
```

Line up the numbers by place value and subtract.

19. 318 – 65 = _____

20. 548 – 109 = _____

21. 783 – 452 = _____

22. 481 – 57 = _____

Circle the correct answer.

23. Store A has 6 packs of 100 stickers, 5 packs
of 10 stickers, and 9 single stickers.
Store B has 5 packs of 100 stickers, 15 packs
of 10 stickers, and 9 single stickers.
Which statement is true?

A. Store A has more stickers than Store B.

B. Store B has more stickers than Store A.

C. Store A and Store B have the same
number of stickers.

Solve.

24. A factory makes 879 hats.
It sells 694 hats in one month.
How many hats does the factory have left?

_____ hats

Name _____

Subtract: Regroup Twice

A store has 324 board games.
It sells 158 board games. How many
board games does the store have left?

Subtract 324 – 158 to find the difference.

Look at the place-value models for this problem.

Line up the numbers by place value to subtract.

Objective
▪ Subtract three-digit numbers, regrouping twice.

Math Words
place value
regroup
ones
tens
hundreds

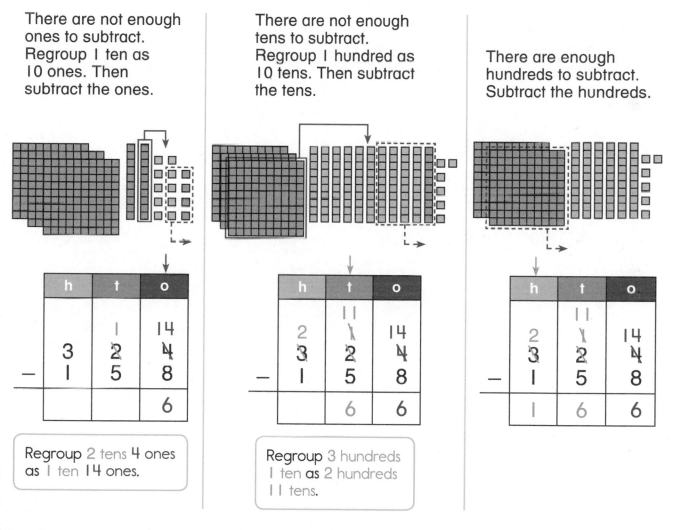

There are not enough ones to subtract. Regroup 1 ten as 10 ones. Then subtract the ones.

There are not enough tens to subtract. Regroup 1 hundred as 10 tens. Then subtract the tens.

There are enough hundreds to subtract. Subtract the hundreds.

h	t	o
	1	14
3	2̶	4̶
– 1	5	8
		6

Regroup 2 tens 4 ones as 1 ten 14 ones.

h	t	o
	11	
2	1̶	14
3̶	2̶	4̶
– 1	5	8
	6	6

Regroup 3 hundreds 1 ten as 2 hundreds 11 tens.

h	t	o
	11	
2	1̶	14
3̶	2̶	4̶
– 1	5	8
1	6	6

▷ The store has 166 board games left.

Subtract. Regroup where needed.

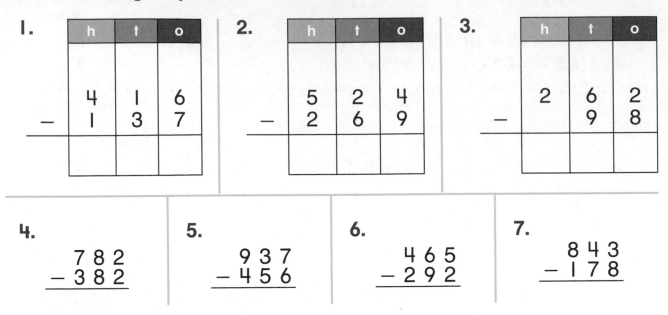

1.

h	t	o
4	1	6
− 1	3	7

2.

h	t	o
5	2	4
− 2	6	9

3.

h	t	o
2	6	2
−	9	8

4.
```
  782
− 382
```

5.
```
  937
− 456
```

6.
```
  465
− 292
```

7.
```
  843
− 178
```

Problem Solving

8. Caleb gets 321 votes in a school election. Zach gets 289 votes. How many more votes does Caleb get than Zach?

   Caleb gets _____ more votes than Zach.

Write About It

9. Lola says that to subtract 854 − 158 she will need to regroup just once because there is enough of every place value except the ones. Is Lola correct? Explain.

   _____

   _____

   _____

Name _____

Subtract: Regroup Twice

$324 - 158 = ?$

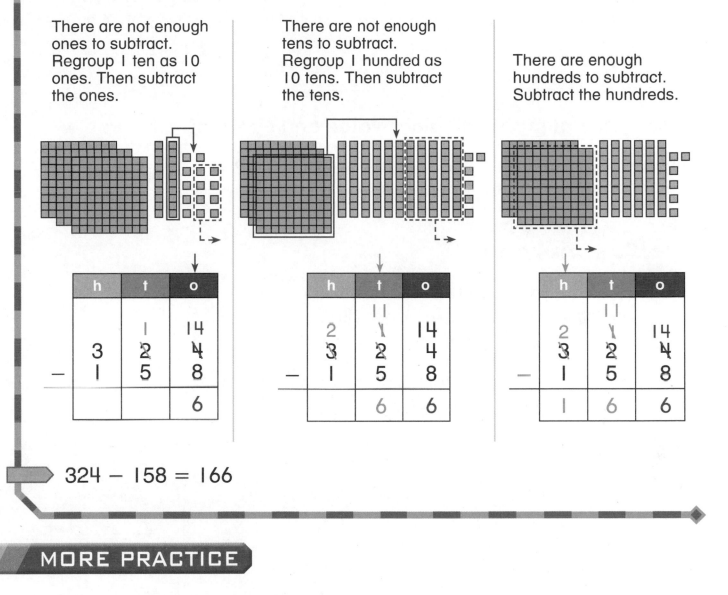

There are not enough ones to subtract. Regroup 1 ten as 10 ones. Then subtract the ones.	There are not enough tens to subtract. Regroup 1 hundred as 10 tens. Then subtract the tens.	There are enough hundreds to subtract. Subtract the hundreds.

h	t	o
3	1⁄2 5	14⁄4 8
− 1	5	8
		6

h	t	o
2⁄3	11 1⁄2 5	14⁄4 8
− 1	5	8
	6	6

h	t	o
2⁄3	11 1⁄2 5	14⁄4 8
− 1	5	8
1	6	6

$324 - 158 = 166$

MORE PRACTICE

Subtract. Regroup where needed.

1.

```
  5 6 3
− 3 7 8
```

2.

```
  6 3 4
− 3 6 5
```

3.

```
  7 9 4
− 4 3 7
```

4.

```
  5 8 4
− 2 9 2
```

Subtract. Regroup where needed.

1.
$$\begin{array}{r} 851 \\ -659 \\ \hline \end{array}$$

2.
$$\begin{array}{r} 935 \\ -47 \\ \hline \end{array}$$

3.
$$\begin{array}{r} 522 \\ -173 \\ \hline \end{array}$$

4.
$$\begin{array}{r} 671 \\ -84 \\ \hline \end{array}$$

Line up the numbers by place value and subtract.

5. $417 - 338 =$ _____

6. $311 - 82 =$ _____

Problem Solving

7. Sarah ran 384 meters and Grace ran 561 meters. How much farther did Grace run than Sarah?

   Grace ran _____ meters farther than Sarah.

Write About It

8. Trevor subtracted $421 - 163$. Is he correct? Explain why or why not. Then write the correct difference if needed.

$$\begin{array}{r} \overset{3}{\cancel{4}}\overset{12}{\cancel{2}}1 \\ -163 \\ \hline 262 \end{array}$$

_____

_____

_____

_____

_____

Subtract: Regroup with Zeros

Objective
■ Subtract three-digit numbers with zeros.

Math Words
regroup
ones
tens
hundreds

There are 300 parking spaces in a parking lot. 127 of the spaces are full. How many spaces are left?

Subtract 300 − 127 to find the difference.

There are not enough ones. There are no tens to regroup.

After you have regrouped, subtract.

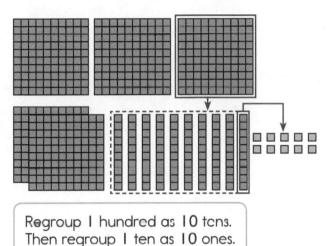

Regroup 1 hundred as 10 tens. Then regroup 1 ten as 10 ones.

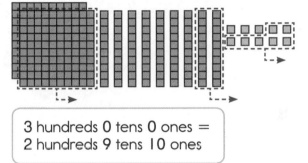

3 hundreds 0 tens 0 ones = 2 hundreds 9 tens 10 ones

Find the difference. Line up the numbers by place value.

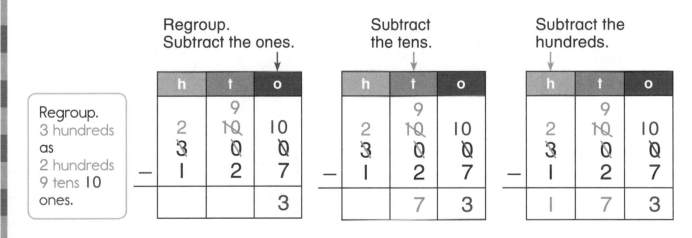

	Regroup. Subtract the ones.	Subtract the tens.	Subtract the hundreds.

Regroup.
3 hundreds
as
2 hundreds
9 tens 10
ones.

Regroup. Subtract the ones.

h	t	o
	9	
2	1̶0̶	10
3̶	0̶	0̶
− 1	2	7
		3

Subtract the tens.

h	t	o
	9	
2	1̶0̶	10
3̶	0̶	0̶
− 1	2	7
	7	3

Subtract the hundreds.

h	t	o
	9	
2	1̶0̶	10
3̶	0̶	0̶
− 1	2	7
1	7	3

There are 173 parking spaces left.

Subtract. Regroup where needed.

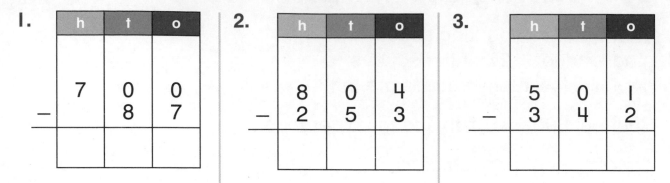

1.
h	t	o
7	0	0
−	8	7

2.
h	t	o
8	0	4
− 2	5	3

3.
h	t	o
5	0	1
− 3	4	2

Subtract. Regroup where needed.

4.
```
  2 0 0
-   3 8
```

5.
```
  7 0 0
- 1 2 8
```

6.
```
  5 0 6
- 1 3 5
```

7.
```
  9 0 7
-   8 8
```

Problem Solving

8. There are 100 math problems on a test. Mark gets 17 problems wrong. How many math problems does Mark get correct?

   Mark gets _____ problems correct.

Write About It

9. Jasmine subtracted 500 − 252. Is she correct? Explain why or why not. Then write the correct difference if needed.

```
  4 10 10
  5 0 0
- 2 5 2
  2 5 8
```

_____

_____

_____

Subtract: Regroup with Zeros

300 − 127 = ?

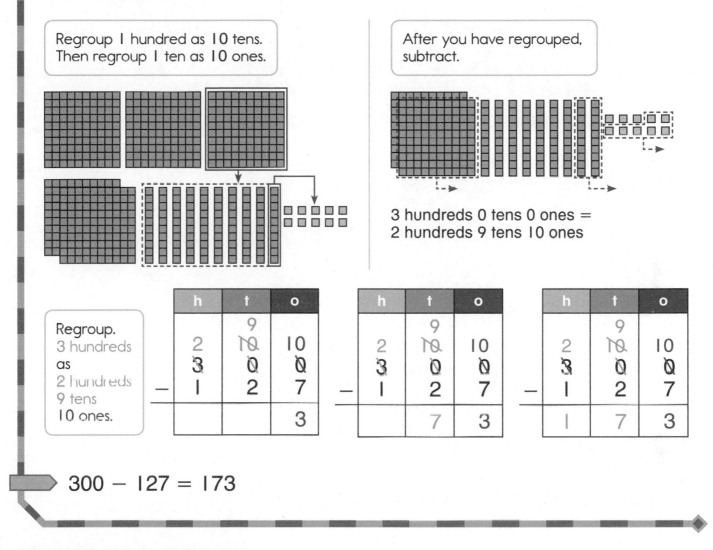

Regroup 1 hundred as 10 tens.
Then regroup 1 ten as 10 ones.

After you have regrouped, subtract.

3 hundreds 0 tens 0 ones =
2 hundreds 9 tens 10 ones

Regroup.
3 hundreds
as
2 hundreds
9 tens
10 ones.

h	t	o
2 3̶	9 1̶0̶ 0	10 0̶ 7
− 1	2	7
		3

h	t	o
2 3̶	9 1̶0̶ 0	10 0̶ 7
− 1	2	7
	7	3

h	t	o
2 3̶	9 1̶0̶ 0	10 0̶ 7
− 1	2	7
1	7	3

▷ 300 − 127 = 173

MORE PRACTICE

Subtract. Regroup where needed.

1.
```
   8 0 0
 − 4 9 1
```

2.
```
   3 0 8
 − 2 3 5
```

3.
```
   3 0 9
 − 1 0 6
```

4.
```
   7 5 0
 −   6 4
```

Subtract. Regroup where needed.

1.
$$
\begin{array}{r} 800 \\ -65 \\ \hline \end{array}
$$

2.
$$
\begin{array}{r} 307 \\ -152 \\ \hline \end{array}
$$

3.
$$
\begin{array}{r} 205 \\ -127 \\ \hline \end{array}
$$

4.
$$
\begin{array}{r} 902 \\ -48 \\ \hline \end{array}
$$

Line up the numbers by place value and subtract.

5. $300 - 128 =$ _____

6. $400 - 68 =$ _____

7. $505 - 119 =$ _____

8. $804 - 79 =$ _____

Problem Solving

9. Nolan has 148 rocks in his collection. He wants to have 200 rocks by the end of the summer. How many more rocks does Nolan need?

   Nolan needs _____ more rocks.

Write About It

10. Chase says that 600 has the same value as 5 hundreds, 9 tens, and 10 ones. Is he correct? Explain.

   _____

   _____

   _____

   _____

Problem Solving Read ⟩ Plan ⟩ Solve ⟩ Check
More Than One Way

Objective
▪ Solve problems by representing the situation in more than one way.

Math Words
model
equation

On Friday, 346 people go to a school play. 57 fewer people go to the play on Saturday. How many people go to the play in all?

The number of people at the play on Saturday is 57 less than 346.

Subtract to find the difference.

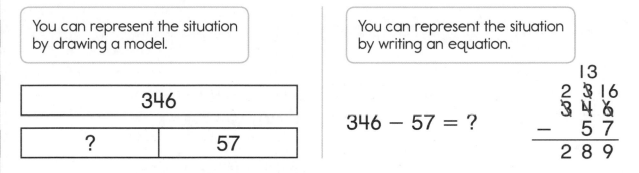

| You can represent the situation by drawing a model. | You can represent the situation by writing an equation. |

346
?	57

$$346 - 57 = \text{?}$$

$$\begin{array}{r} {\scriptstyle 13} \\ {\scriptstyle 2\ 3\ 16} \\ \cancel{3}\ \cancel{4}\ \cancel{6} \\ -\ \ 5\ 7 \\ \hline 2\ 8\ 9 \end{array}$$

There are 289 people at the play on Saturday.

346 people go to the play on Friday and 289 people go on Saturday. How many people go to the play in all?

Add to find the answer.

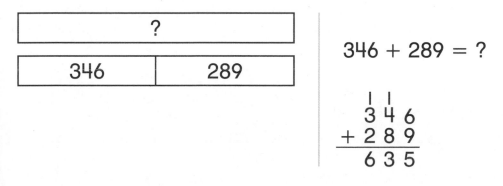

?
346	289

$$346 + 289 = \text{?}$$

$$\begin{array}{r} {\scriptstyle 1\ \ 1} \\ 3\ 4\ 6 \\ +\ 2\ 8\ 9 \\ \hline 6\ 3\ 5 \end{array}$$

▷ 635 people go to the play in all.

Read each problem. Represent each situation with models or equations to help you solve the problem.

1. Jenna has 294 coins. She has 25 more coins than Emily. How many coins do the girls have in all?

The girls have _____ coins in all.

2. Brian, Gavin, and Julio each have a different mystery number. The sum of the three numbers is 170. Julio's number is 86 less than the sum. Brian's number is 14 more than Gavin's. Gavin's number is 48 less than Julio's. What is each boy's number?

Julio's number is _____.   Gavin's number is _____.

Brian's number is _____.

Write About It

3. Explain the strategy you used to solve the problem above.

_____

_____

_____

_____

Problem Solving
More Than One Way

On Friday, 346 people go to a school play.
57 fewer people go to the play on Saturday.
How many people go to the play on Friday
and Saturday?

The number of people at the play on Saturday
is 57 less than 346.

You can represent the situation by drawing
a model or writing an equation.

Subtract to find the difference.

346	
?	57

$346 - 57 = ?$

$$\begin{array}{r} {\overset{13}{}} \\ 2\ \overset{\cancel{3}}{}\ 16 \\ \cancel{3}\ \cancel{4}\ \cancel{6} \\ -\ \ 5\ 7 \\ \hline 2\ 8\ 9 \end{array}$$

There are 289 people at the play on Saturday.

346 people go to the play on Friday
and 289 people go on Saturday.
How many people go to the play on
Friday and Saturday?

Add to find the answer.

?	
346	289

$346 + 289 = ?$

$$\begin{array}{r} {\overset{1}{}\ \overset{1}{}} \\ 3\ 4\ 6 \\ +\ 2\ 8\ 9 \\ \hline 6\ 3\ 5 \end{array}$$

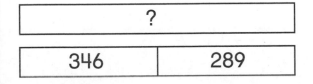 635 people go to the play in all.

Solve. You can represent the situation with models or equations to help you.

I. A tailor starts the month with 900 buttons.
   The first week he uses 82 buttons.
   The next week he uses 123 buttons.
   How many buttons does he have left?

   The tailor has _____ buttons left.

2. Sandeep uses these cards to make a three-digit number. How many three-digit numbers less than 500 can he make?

   Sandeep can make ____ numbers.

   List the numbers in order from greatest to least.

   _____

3. Alexis wants to find the sum of two numbers that have a difference of 135. The greater of the two numbers is 327. Alexis says that the sum is 462. Is she correct? Explain why or why not.

   _____

   _____

   _____

   _____

LESSON 9-8

HOMEWORK

The table shows the number of hours each class reads in a read-a-thon. Use the table to answer Problems 1–4. You can use models or equations to represent each situation.

Class	Hours of Reading
A	168
B	154
C	201
D	172
E	200

1. What is the difference between the greatest and least numbers of hours spent reading?

   _____ hours

2. How many hours in all did the classes spend reading?

   _____ hours

3. What is the difference between the total number of hours Classes A and B spent reading and the total number of hours Classes C and E spent reading?

   The difference is _____ hours.

4. How many more hours would Class D have to read to reach the same number of hours as Class E?

   Class D would have to read _____ more hours.

Solve. You can represent the situation with models or equations to help you.

5. Nicole has some songs on her music player. She downloads 123 more songs. Then she deletes 15 songs. Now she has 500 songs. How many songs did she have on her music player to start?

   Nicole had _____ songs to start.

6. Two numbers have a sum of 700. One of the numbers is 127. What is the difference of the two numbers?

   The difference of the numbers is _____.

7. Four friends have a swimming race. Mya is not the fastest, but she is also not the slowest. Adriana finishes before Mya, but after Summer. Peyton is the slowest swimmer. In what order do the friends finish the race?

   _____

Write About It

8. Explain the strategy you used to solve the earlier problem in which the sum of two numbers is 700 and you have to find the difference.

   _____

   _____

   _____

   _____

Name_____

Use Addition to Check Subtraction: Three-Digit Numbers

Objective
■ Use addition to check three-digit subtraction.

Math Words
add
subtract
difference

In a town, 500 children play soccer and 368 children play basketball. How many more children play soccer than basketball?

Subtract to find how many more children play soccer.

You can add to check your subtraction.

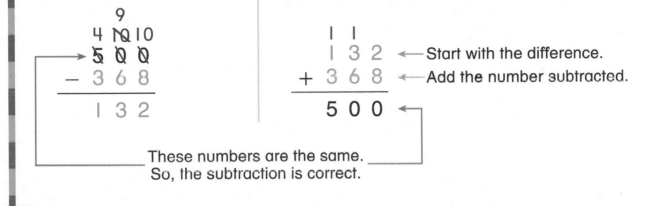

Subtract 500 − 368.　　　Add to check the answer.

132 ← Start with the difference.
+ 368 ← Add the number subtracted.
500 ←

These numbers are the same. So, the subtraction is correct.

➤ 132 more children play soccer than basketball.

PRACTICE

Match the subtraction problem to the addition problem that you can use to check it.

1. 448 − 319 = 129 　　　　　**A.** 190 + 129 = 319

2. 319 − 129 = 190 　　　　　**B.** 129 + 319 = 448

3. 509 − 190 = 319 　　　　　**C.** 319 + 190 = 509

Subtract. Add to check.

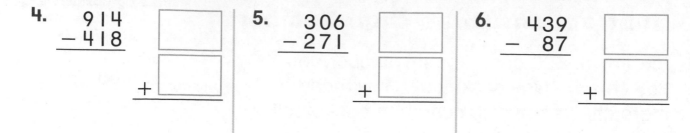

4.
```
   9 1 4
 − 4 1 8
```
□
+ □

5.
```
   3 0 6
 − 2 7 1
```
□
+ □

6.
```
   4 3 9
 −   8 7
```
□
+ □

Problem Solving

7. A stadium has 500 tickets to sell for a game. The day before the game, they have 82 tickets left. How many tickets did the stadium sell? Write your answer. Then write an addition equation to check your answer.

The stadium sold _____ tickets.

_____ + _____ = _____

Write About It

8. Hannah subtracted $437 − 212 = 225$.
   To check her answer, she added $225 + 437$.
   Explain what Hannah did wrong. Then write the correct addition problem for Hannah to use.

_____

_____

_____

_____

Name _____

Use Addition to Check Subtraction: Three-Digit Numbers

$500 - 368 = ?$

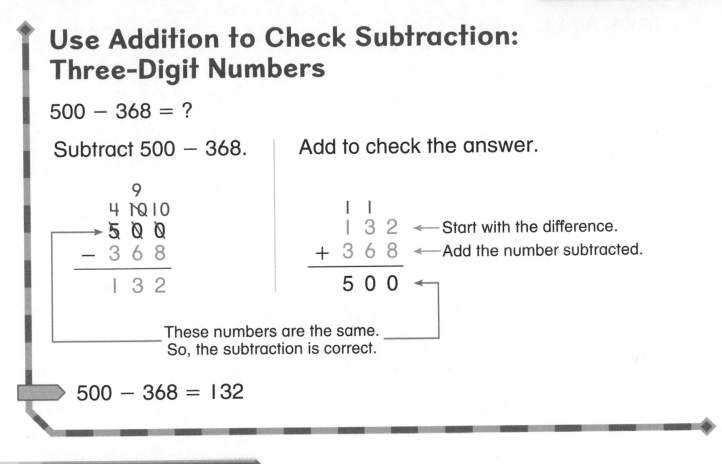

Subtract 500 − 368.

Add to check the answer.

```
        9
    4 ⱪⱪ10
    5 0 0
  − 3 6 8
    1 3 2
```

```
      1 1
      1 3 2   ←Start with the difference.
    + 3 6 8   ←Add the number subtracted.
      5 0 0
```

These numbers are the same.
So, the subtraction is correct.

$500 - 368 = 132$

MORE PRACTICE

Match the subtraction problem to the addition problem that you can use to check it.

1. $321 - 246 = 75$

2. $396 - 75 = 321$

3. $567 - 321 = 246$

A. $75 + 246 = 321$

B. $246 + 321 = 567$

C. $321 + 75 = 396$

4.
```
    826
  − 342   ☐
  +        ☐
```

5.
```
    405
  − 164   ☐
  +        ☐
```

Subtract. Add to check.

1.
$$\begin{array}{r} 865 \\ -683 \\ \hline \end{array}$$
□
+ □

2.
$$\begin{array}{r} 360 \\ -294 \\ \hline \end{array}$$
□
+ □

3.
$$\begin{array}{r} 426 \\ -109 \\ \hline \end{array}$$
□
+ □

Problem Solving

4. A football team ran 585 yards at practice on Monday. On Tuesday, the team ran 128 yards less. How many yards did the team run on Tuesday? Write a subtraction equation to find your answer. Then write an addition equation to check your answer.

_____ − _____ = _____

_____ + _____ = _____

The football team ran _____ yards on Tuesday.

┌─ Write About It ─────────────────────

5. You can use addition to check subtraction. Can you use subtraction to check addition? Explain.

_____

_____

_____

_____

Continue the pattern. Write −1, −10, or −100 to explain the pattern.

1. 303, 302, 301, _____   Pattern: _____

2. 681, 581, 481, _____   Pattern: _____

3. 710, 700, 690, _____   Pattern: _____

Subtract.

4.   885
   − 124

5.   768
   − 315

6.   477
   − 52

7.   909
   − 104

Subtract. Regroup where needed.

8.   562
   − 245

9.   768
   − 39

10.   641
    − 419

11.   223
    − 107

Regroup 1 hundred as 10 tens. Write the new number of hundreds, tens, and ones.

12. 5 hundreds 3 tens 9 ones = _____ hundreds _____ tens _____ ones

13. 7 hundreds 0 tens 0 ones = _____ hundreds _____ tens _____ ones

14. 6 hundreds 8 tens 5 ones = _____ hundreds _____ tens _____ ones

Subtract. Regroup where needed.

15.
```
  6 4 2
- 3 7 0
```

16.
```
  8 2 7
- 7 3 6
```

17.
```
  9 1 2
-   8 5
```

18.
```
  3 4 3
- 1 5 9
```

Line up the numbers by place value and subtract.

19. 500 − 36 = _____

20. 703 − 259 = _____

21. 209 − 132 = _____

22. 800 − 551 = _____

Subtract. Add to check.

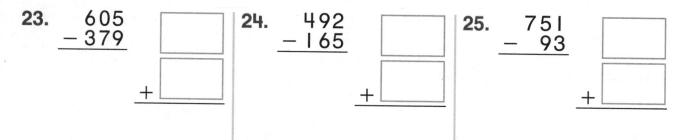

23.
```
  6 0 5
- 3 7 9
```

24.
```
  4 9 2
- 1 6 5
```

25.
```
  7 5 1
-   9 3
```

Solve.

26. The sum of two numbers is 750. The lesser of the two numbers is 173. What is the difference of the two numbers? Represent the situation with models or equations to help you solve the problem.

The difference is _____.

A family is choosing a new refrigerator. The amount of energy each refrigerator uses is measured in kilowatt hours (kWh).

Refrigerators	
Model	**Energy Use (kWh per year)**
A	314
B	700
C	685

1. A refrigerator that uses less energy is more efficient. What is the difference in energy use between the most efficient and least efficient refrigerators? Explain how you found your answer.

   The difference is _____ kWh per year.

   _____

   _____

   _____

2. A salesperson tells the family that Model A uses less energy in 2 years than Model C uses in 1 year. Is the salesperson right? Explain. Find the difference in the amount of energy Model C uses in 1 year and Model A uses in 2 years.

   _____

   _____

   _____

   _____

Name _____

Determine the best answer for the problem.

1. Subtract.

$35 - 14 =$ _____

2. Use mental math to subtract.
$230 - 50 =$?

   A. 170
   B. 180
   C. 225
   D. 280

3. Add.

$8 + 5 + 2 =$?

   A. 13
   B. 14
   C. 15
   D. 16

4. Subtract.

$$\begin{array}{r} 7\,5 \\ -\,2\,9 \\ \hline \end{array}$$

5. Which three answers are equal to 12?

   A. $2 + 10$
   B. $3 + 9$
   C. $5 + 8$
   D. $7 + 5$

6. Which two answers are equal to 6?

   A. $9 - 4$
   B. $11 - 5$
   C. $12 - 6$
   D. $14 - 7$

7. Write 683 in expanded form.

_____ + ____ + ___

8. A diner makes 87 muffins for breakfast. It sells 56 of them. How many are left?

_____ muffins

Foundations for Multiplication

CHAPTER 10

Take a deep breath. Did you know that trees help clean the air you breathe? Trees are beautiful, and they are helpful too. They improve water quality and help control flooding. They provide fruit and shade. Many kinds of animals use trees as their homes.

Types of Trees

♦ The leaves of deciduous trees come in many sizes and shapes. They change colors in different seasons.

♦ The narrow, needle-like leaves of coniferous trees stay green all year.

Clues to the Past

♦ As scientists study the ages of trees, they learn about how weather makes changes on earth.

♦ Find out how scientists can calculate the ages of trees without cutting them down.

Dear Family,

In this chapter, we will be learning about odd and even numbers and using arrays.

Here are the key **Math Words** for this chapter:

even	**row**
odd	**column**
equal addends	**equation**
array	

You can use the glossary to find the definition of each word and help your child make flash cards to study each day we work on the lessons for this chapter.

During this chapter we will also be making STEAM (Science, Technology, Engineering, the Arts, and Mathematics) connections about numbers in nature. Read the opening to the chapter together.

Keep Your Skills Sharp

Here is a **Keep Your Skills Sharp** activity to do at home to prepare for this chapter.

Have your child find pairs of objects, such as socks, forks and spoons, or bowls and plates, when folding laundry or setting the table. Discuss pairs and ask whether or not each object is part of a pair. Help your child describe the number of socks, or place settings at the table, as being odd or even.

Name_____

Odd and Even Numbers

Objective
- Count objects by 2s, or pair objects, to decide if a number is odd or even.

Math Words
odd
even

Emma picks 7 carrots and 6 tomatoes. Does she pick an odd or an even number of each food?

To find out if the number of each type of food is odd or even, you can count by 2s or make pairs.

If there is 1 left over, the number is odd.
If there is nothing left over, the number is even.

Count by 2s

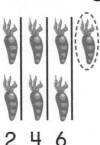
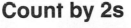

2 4 6

2 4 6

Make Pairs

There is 1
left over.

Nothing is
left over.

There is 1
left over.

Nothing is
left over.

> Emma picks an odd number of carrots and an even number of tomatoes.

PRACTICE

Circle *even* or *odd*.

1. Count by 2s.
   Is 8 even or odd?

even

odd

_____

2. Make pairs.
   Is 11 even or odd?

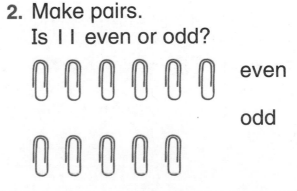

even

odd

Make pairs or count by 2s. Write *even* or *odd*.

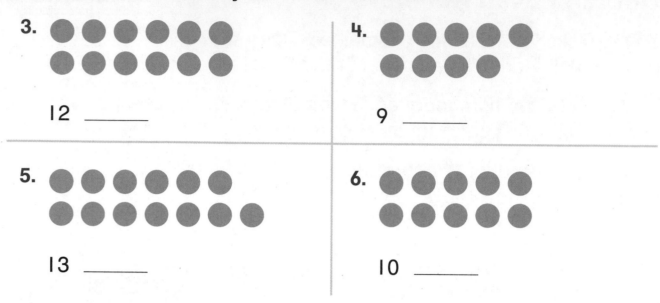

3. 12 _____

4. 9 _____

5. 13 _____

6. 10 _____

Problem Solving

7. Joel says that 14 is an odd number because when he puts 14 objects in pairs there are 2 left over. Is Joel correct? Explain.

_____

_____

Write About It

8. Abigail picks an odd number of red plums and an odd number of purple plums. Is the total number of plums odd or even? Explain how you know.

_____

_____

Odd and Even Numbers

To tell if a number is odd or even,
count by 2s or make pairs.

If there is 1 left over, the number is odd.
If there is nothing left over, the number is even.

| **Count by 2s** | | **Make Pairs** | |

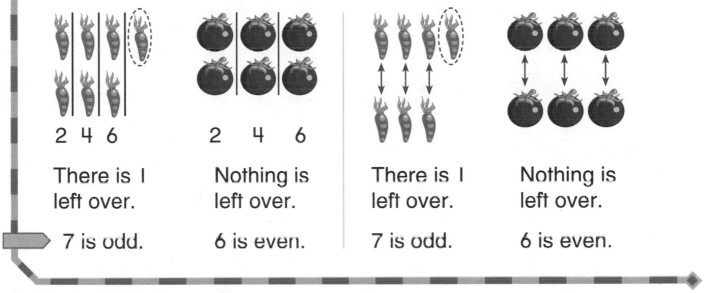

| 2 4 6 | 2 4 6 | | |

There is 1 left over.	Nothing is left over.	There is 1 left over.	Nothing is left over.
7 is odd.	6 is even.	7 is odd.	6 is even.

MORE PRACTICE

Circle *even* or *odd*.

1. Count by 2s.
   Is 9 even or odd?

even

odd

_____ _____ _____ _____

2. Make pairs.
   Is 12 even or odd?

even

odd

Count by 2s or make pairs. Write _even_ or _odd_.

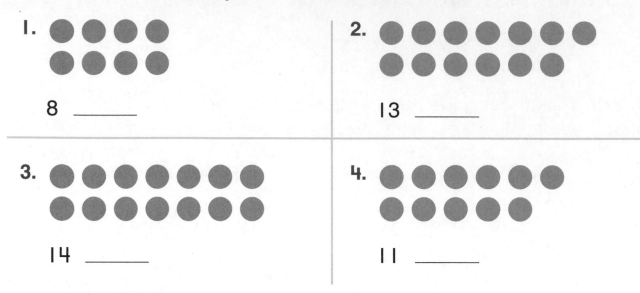

1. 8 _____

2. 13 _____

3. 14 _____

4. 11 _____

Problem Solving

5. Jeremy is thinking of a two-digit number.
   The number is even. It is greater than 16.
   There is a 1 in the tens place.
   What is Jeremy's number?
   Draw counters to show the number
   counting by 2s or making pairs.

   Jeremy's number is _____.

Write About It

6. Explain how counting by 2s and making
   pairs are alike.

   _____

   _____

   _____

   _____

Name _____

Represent Even Numbers

Objective
- Write an even number as the sum of two equal addends.

Math Words

odd
even
equal addends

Peter has 6 green pencils and 9 blue pencils. Does he have an even or an odd number of each color of pencil?

Even numbers are the sum of two equal addends.

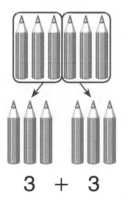

3 + 3

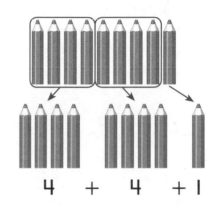

4 + 4 + 1

If you can make two equal groups, the number is even.

If you cannot make two equal groups, the number is odd.

> Peter has an even number of green pencils.
> He has an odd number of blue pencils.

PRACTICE

Write *even* or *odd*. If the number is even, write it as the sum of two equal addends.

I.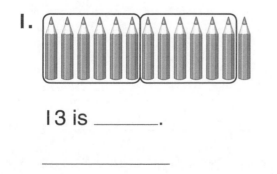

13 is _____.

_____

2.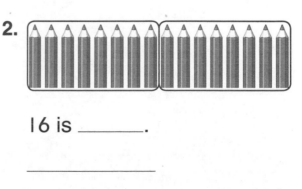

16 is _____.

_____

Write *even* or *odd*. If the number is even, write it as the sum of two equal addends.

3. 7 is _____.

_____

4. 10 is _____.

_____

5. 14 is _____.

_____

Problem Solving

6. What digits can be in the ones place of an even number?

_____

7. Lydia's mystery number is an odd number less than 20. It has 6 more ones than tens. What is Lydia's mystery number?

Lydia's number is _____.

Write About It

8. Olive says 12 is not an even number. She says it is odd because you can add 5 + 7, which are not the same, to get 12. What is Olive's mistake?

_____

_____

_____

Represent Even Numbers

Even numbers are the sum of two equal addends.

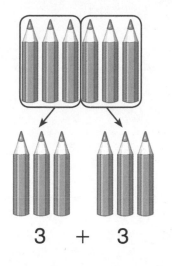

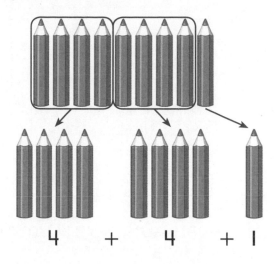

3 + 3	4 + 4 + 1
There are 2 equal groups.	There is 1 left over.
If you can make two equal groups, the number is even.	If you cannot make two equal groups, the number is odd.
$3 + 3 = 6$	
6 is even.	9 is odd.

MORE PRACTICE

Write *even* or *odd*. If the number is even, write it as the sum of two equal addends.

1.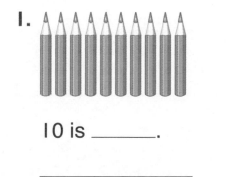

10 is _____.

_____

2.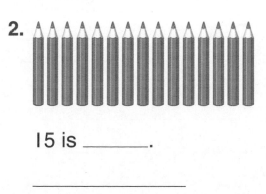

15 is _____.

_____

Write *even* or *odd*. If the number is even, write it as the sum of two equal addends.

1. 17 is _____.
_____

2. 8 is _____.
_____

3. 5 is _____.
_____

4. 20 is _____.
_____

5. 19 is _____.
_____

6. 4 is _____.
_____

Circle the even numbers. Draw a line under the odd numbers.

7. 13   9   2   18   11

8. 12   16   19   10   3

Problem Solving

9. Jake's mystery number is greater than 8 and less than 20. It has 3 more ones than tens. What is Jake's mystery number? Is it even or odd?

   Jake's number is _____. It is _____.

Write About It

10. Is the sum of 9 + 9 even or odd? Explain how you know.

_____

_____

_____

Name _____

Make pairs or count by 2s.
Write *even* or *odd*.

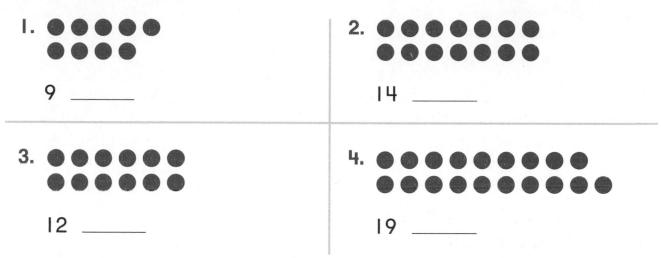

1. 9 _____

2. 14 _____

3. 12 _____

4. 19 _____

Solve.

5. Colin solves 11 math problems. Then he solves 5 more math problems. Does Colin solve an even number or an odd number of math problems? How many math problems does he solve in all?

   Colin solves an _____ number of math problems.

   He solves _____ math problems in all.

6. Marcos has an odd number of shells in his collection. Then he finds an even number of shells at the beach. Does Marcos have an even number or an odd number of shells in all?

   Marcos has an _____ number of shells in all.

Write _even_ or _odd_. If the number is even, write it as the sum of two equal addends.

7. 5 is _____.	8. 12 is _____.	9. 17 is _____.
_____	_____	_____
10. 15 is _____.	11. 16 is _____.	12. 22 is _____.
_____	_____	_____

Circle the number that has the same value as the group of addends.

13. 4 + 4 + 1

    A. 8

    B. 9

    C. 13

14. 9 + 9

    A. 16

    B. 17

    C. 18

Circle the letter next to the true statement.

15. **A.** The digit in the ones place of an even number can be 0, 2, 4, 5, or 8.

    B. A number that has a 0 in the ones place can be either odd or even.

    C. The digit in the ones place of an odd number can be 1, 3, 5, 7, or 9.

Name _____

Arrays: Repeated Addition

Rebecca arranges her leaf collection in 3 rows. There are 5 leaves in each row. How many leaves does Rebecca have in her collection?

An array is an arrangement of objects in rows and columns. Each row has the same number of objects. Each column has the same number of objects.

Objective
- Use addition with equal addends to find the number of objects in an array.

Math Words
array
row
column

You can add the objects in each row:

$$\begin{array}{r} 5 \\ 5 \\ + 5 \\ \hline 15 \end{array}$$

The sum is the same.

You can add the objects in each column:

$$3 + 3 + 3 + 3 + 3 = 15$$

> Rebecca has 15 leaves in her collection.

PRACTICE

Complete two equations for the array.

1.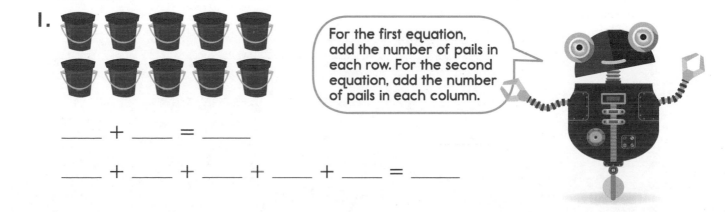

For the first equation, add the number of pails in each row. For the second equation, add the number of pails in each column.

____ + ____ = ____

____ + ____ + ____ + ____ + ____ = ____

Write two equations for each array.
Find how many in all.

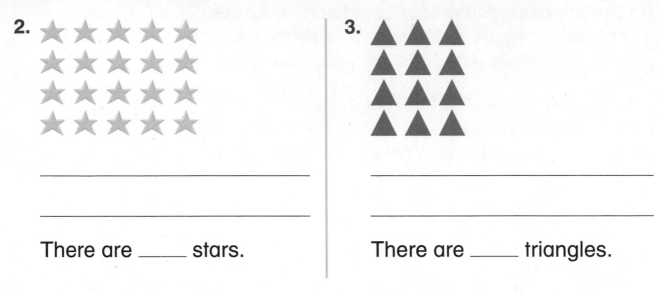

2.

_____

_____

There are _____ stars.

3.

_____

_____

There are _____ triangles.

Problem Solving

4. Molly makes an array with 5 rows
of shells. There are 2 shells in each row.
How many shells does Molly have?

   Molly has _____ shells.

Write About It

5. Why is the sum in an array the same whether you
add the numbers in each column or the numbers
in each row?

_____

_____

_____

_____

Name _____

Arrays: Repeated Addition

An array is an arrangement of objects in rows and columns. Each row has the same number of objects. Each column has the same number of objects.

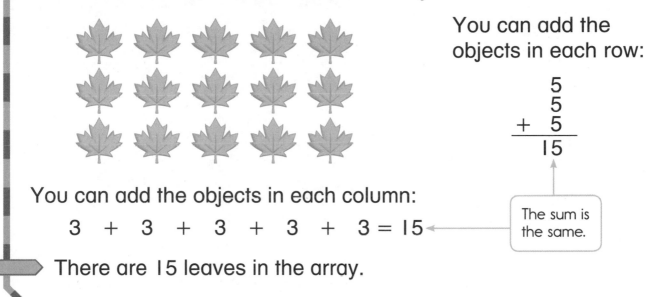

You can add the objects in each row:

$$
\begin{array}{r}
5 \\
5 \\
+\ 5 \\
\hline
15
\end{array}
$$

The sum is the same.

You can add the objects in each column:

3 + 3 + 3 + 3 + 3 = 15

> There are 15 leaves in the array.

MORE PRACTICE

Circle the two groups of addends that tell the total number of diamonds in the array.

I.

3 + 5

3 + 3 + 3 + 3 + 3

5 + 5 + 5

6 + 6 + 6

There are _____ diamonds in the array.

Write two equations for each array.
Find how many in all.

1.  ★ ★ ★ ★
   ★ ★ ★ ★
   ★ ★ ★ ★

   _____

   _____

   There are _____ stars.

2.  ▲ ▲ ▲ ▲
   ▲ ▲ ▲ ▲

   _____

   _____

   There are _____ triangles.

Problem Solving

3. Jeremiah makes an array with 25 toy trucks.
   There are 5 columns of trucks. How many trucks
   does Jeremiah put in each row?

   Jeremiah puts _____ trucks in each row.

Write About It

4. When you make an array and then write an
   equation to find the total, why are the addends
   all the same number?

   _____

   _____

   _____

   _____

Name_____

Arrays: Show the Same Number

Ben has 4 rows of photos. Each row has 3 photos. Ben wants to put the photos in 3 equal rows. How many photos should he put in each row?

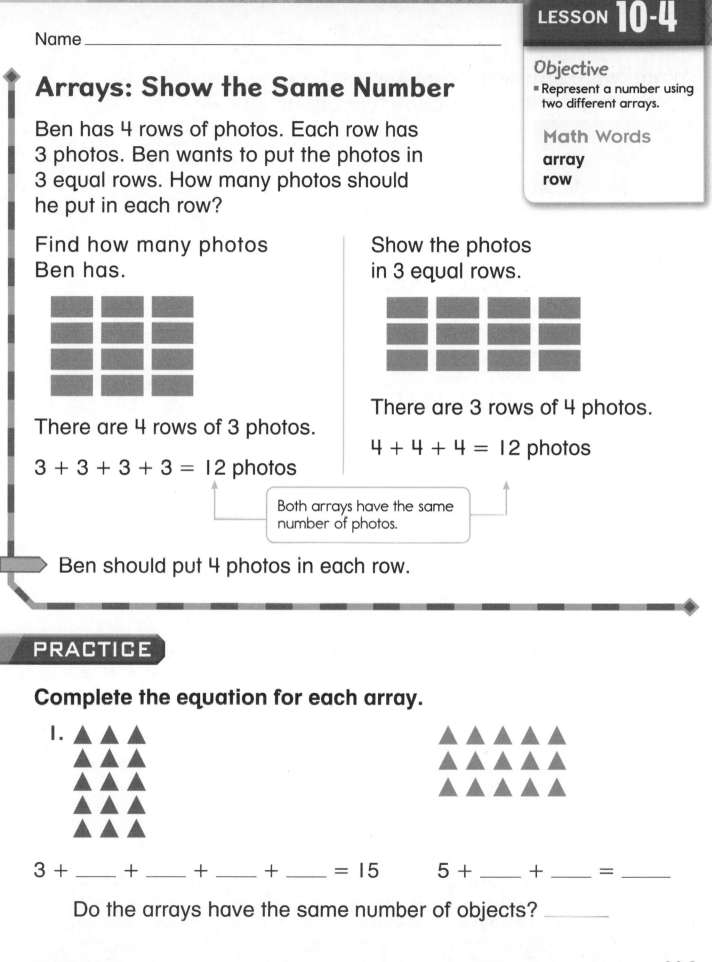

Find how many photos Ben has.

There are 4 rows of 3 photos.

$3 + 3 + 3 + 3 = 12$ photos

Show the photos in 3 equal rows.

There are 3 rows of 4 photos.

$4 + 4 + 4 = 12$ photos

Both arrays have the same number of photos.

Ben should put 4 photos in each row.

PRACTICE

Complete the equation for each array.

1.

$3 + \underline{\quad} + \underline{\quad} + \underline{\quad} + \underline{\quad} = 15$ $5 + \underline{\quad} + \underline{\quad} = \underline{\quad}$

Do the arrays have the same number of objects? _____

Draw a different array that has the same number of objects. Write an equation for your array.

2.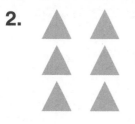

_____

Describe two arrays that have the given number of objects.

3. 16 marbles   ____ rows of ____ marbles

      ____ rows of ____ marbles

Problem Solving

4. Ricardo made an array with 2 rows of 9 cards. How many cards are in his array?

   ____ cards

   Describe a different array that has the same number of cards.

   _____

Write About It

5. Explain how an array with 4 rows of 5 objects and an array with 5 rows of 4 objects are the same. Then explain how they are different.

   _____

   _____

   _____

Name _____

Arrays: Show the Same Number

Does an array with 4 rows of 3 objects have the
same number as an array with 3 rows of 4 objects?

How many is 4 rows of 3?

$3 + 3 + 3 + 3 = 12$

How many is 3 rows of 4?

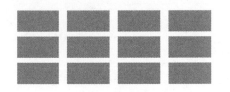

$4 + 4 + 4 = 12$

Yes. Both arrays have the same number of objects.

MORE PRACTICE

**Draw a different array that has the same
number of objects as the one shown.
Write an equation for your array.**

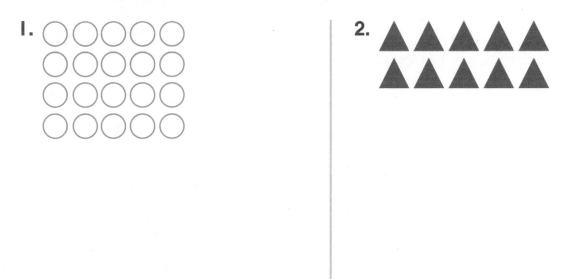

1.

2.

_____   _____

Describe two arrays that have the given number of objects.

1. 8 stamps   ____ rows of ____ stamps

                   ____ rows of ____ stamps

2. 10 pencils   ____ rows of ____ pencils

                   ____ rows of ____ pencils

3. 16 erasers   ____ rows of ____ erasers

                   ____ rows of ____ erasers

Problem Solving

4. Alan and Blake build arrays with blocks. Alan's array has 6 rows with 2 blocks in each row. Blake's array has 4 rows with 3 blocks in each row. How many blocks did each boy use?

Each boy used ____ blocks.

Write About It

5. How do you make an array for a given number of objects?

_____

_____

_____

_____

Name _____

Problem Solving ⟩Read⟩ ⟩Plan⟩ ⟩Solve⟩ ⟩Check⟩
Draw a Picture

Objectives
- Solve problems by drawing a picture.
- Use a variety of strategies to solve problems.

Math Words

row

column

Cesar buys 3 boxes of markers.
Each box has 5 markers in it.
Isaac buys 4 boxes of markers.
Each box has 4 markers in it.
Who buys more markers?

You can draw a picture to show the total number of markers each boy buys.

The number of rows shows the number of boxes. The number of columns shows the number of markers in each box.

Cesar: 3 boxes of 5   Isaac: 4 boxes of 4

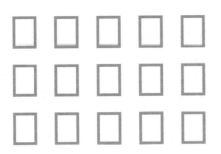

$5 + 5 + 5 = 15$

Cesar buys a total of 15 markers.

$4 + 4 + 4 + 4 = 16$

Isaac buys a total of 16 markers.

$15 < 16$

⟩ Isaac buys more markers.

Read and solve each problem. You can draw a picture to help solve some of the problems.

1. Mr. Hill plants 2 rows of 5 tulips. He also plants 3 rows of 3 daisies. Does Mr. Hill plant more tulips or daisies? Draw a picture and solve.

Mr. Hill plants more _____.

2. The library sets up a display with 5 rows of books. Each row has 4 books in it. At the end of the day, 13 of the books have been checked out. How many books are left? Draw a picture and solve.

There are _____ books left in the display.

Write About It

3. Explain the strategy you used to find the number of books left in the library's display.

_____

_____

_____

Problem Solving
Draw a Picture

Cesar buys 3 boxes of markers. Each box has
5 markers in it. Isaac buys 4 boxes of markers.
Each box has 4 markers in it. Who buys more markers?

You can draw a picture to show the problem.

Cesar: 3 boxes of 5

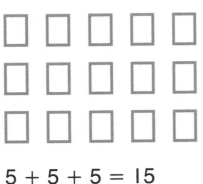

$5 + 5 + 5 = 15$

Isaac: 4 boxes of 4

$4 + 4 + 4 + 4 = 16$

Isaac buys more markers.

MORE PRACTICE

Draw a picture to help solve the problem.

1. A teacher has 24 bins of books.
   She puts the bins in 4 rows.
   How many bins are in each row?

   There are ____ bins in each row.

2. Luke has 3 rows of pictures on a wall in his room. There are 4 pictures in each row. His sister also has the same number of pictures in her room. How many pictures are there in both rooms in all? Draw a picture and solve.

There are _____ pictures in all.

---

3. Amy's basketball team scored 386 points last season. This season the team scored 38 fewer points than last season. How many points in all did Amy's team score during the two seasons? Show your solution.

Amy's team scored _____ points in all for the two seasons.

---

4. Macy's lock has a three-digit passcode. She knows that the digits are 5, 0, and 9, but she cannot remember the order. What are all the possible passcodes?

HOMEWORK

Read and solve each problem. You can draw a picture to help solve some of the problems.

1. Fernando buys 3 boxes of blueberry bars that have 6 bars each. He also buys 2 boxes of strawberry bars that have 7 bars each. Does Fernando buy more blueberry or more strawberry bars? Draw a picture and solve.

   Fernando buys more _____ bars.

2. Art students hang their paintings in 5 rows of 5 to dry. At the end of the week, 17 students take their paintings home. How many paintings are left to dry? Draw a picture and solve.

   There are ____ paintings left to dry.

3. Ben has 4 rows of buttons, with 2 buttons in each row.
Mark has 2 rows of buttons, with 6 buttons in each row.
How many more buttons does Ben need in order to have
the same number as Mark? Draw a picture and solve.

Ben needs _____ more buttons.

4. Two numbers have a sum of 560.
One of the numbers is 184.
What is the difference of the two numbers?

The difference is _____.

Write About It

5. Explain the strategy you use to find the difference
of two numbers when you know their sum and the
value of one of the numbers.

_____

_____

_____

_____

Name_____

Make pairs or count by 2s.
Write *odd* or *even*.

1.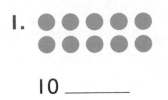

10 _____

2. ●●●●●●●●
●●●●●●●

17 _____

Write *odd* or *even*. If the number is even,
write it as the sum of two equal addends.

3. 9 is _____.

_____

4. 14 is _____.

_____

5. 18 is _____.

_____

Write two equations for each array.
Find how many in all.

6. ★★★★★
★★★★★
★★★★★

_____

_____

There are _____ stars.

7. ▲▲▲▲▲
▲▲▲▲
▲▲▲▲
▲▲▲▲

_____

_____

There are _____ triangles.

Draw a different array that has the same number of objects as the one shown. Write an equation for your array.

8.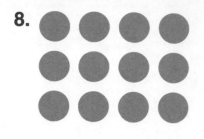

_____

9.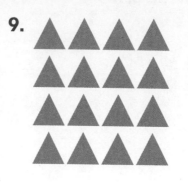

_____

Describe two arrays that have the given number of objects.

10. 18 muffins

_____ rows of _____ muffins

_____ rows of _____ muffins

Solve.

11. A store orders 3 boxes of shirts. Each box holds 9 shirts. In the first hour after the boxes are unpacked, the store sells 8 of the shirts. How many shirts are left? Draw a picture and solve.

There are _____ shirts left.

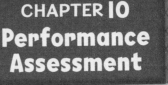

Name _____

Chloe finds a leaf from a sugar maple tree in her backyard.

1. There are 7 veins that connect at the stem. Is the number of veins on the leaf even or odd? How do you know?

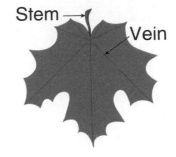

_____

_____

_____

_____

2. There are 18 points around the edge of the leaf. Is the number of points even or odd? How do you know?

_____

_____

_____

3. Go on a nature walk with your parent or teacher. Collect different leaves around your backyard, neighborhood, or school.

   • For each leaf you collect, use numbers in at least two different ways to describe what you can see on the leaf.

   • Decide if each number in your description is odd or even, and explain how you know.

   Share your leaves and findings with your class.

Name _____

Determine the best answer for each problem.

1. Subtract.

   $15 - 9 = ?$

   A. 6
   B. 7
   C. 8
   D. 9

2. Add.

   $27 + 14 = ?$

   A. 40
   B. 41
   C. 42
   D. 43

3. Add.

   $\begin{array}{r} 9 \\ 6 \\ + 8 \\ \hline \end{array}$

   A. 21
   B. 22
   C. 23
   D. 24

4. Subtract.

   $\begin{array}{r} 47 \\ - 28 \\ \hline \end{array}$

   A. 19
   B. 21
   C. 27
   D. 29

5. Write the missing number in the equation.

   $25 + \underline{\quad} = 32$

6. Write the missing number in the equation.

   $43 - \underline{\quad} = 28$

7. Write 719 in expanded form.

   $\underline{\quad} + \underline{\quad} + \underline{\quad}$

8. Compare the numbers.

   809 ⟮ ? ⟯ 891

   A. >
   B. <
   C. =

Data and Graphical Displays

Plastic trash can end up in the ocean. This plastic hurts sea animals.

Birds and seals get tangled in plastic. Fish and turtles eat plastic that looks like food.

By the Numbers

◆ Half of the sea turtles in the world have eaten plastic.

◆ An American family takes home about 125 plastic bags each month.

◆ 25 plastic bottles can be used to make a fleece jacket.

What You Can Do

◆ Use refillable water bottles.

◆ Bring reusable bags to the grocery store.

◆ Recycle plastic instead of throwing it in the trash.

Dear Family,

In this chapter, we will be learning about data and graphical displays.

Here are the key **Math Words** for this chapter:

line plot	symbol
data	key
tally chart	bar graph
tally mark	model
picture graph	

You can use the glossary to find the definition of each word and help your child make flashcards to study each day we work on the lessons for this chapter.

During this chapter about data and graphs, we will also be making STEAM (Science, Technology, Engineering, the Arts, and Mathematics) connections about recycling and the oceans. Read the opening to the chapter together.

Keep Your Skills Sharp

Here is a **Keep Your Skills Sharp** activity to do at home to prepare for this chapter.

Have your child sort objects into categories, such as forks, knives, and spoons, while washing the dishes or emptying the dishwasher. Once the objects have been sorted into categories, have your child count and record the number of objects in each category.

Name _____

Read Line Plots

Objective
- Read and interpret line plots.

Math Words
line plot
data

A group of children listed their heights to the nearest inch. What does the line plot show about the heights of the children?

A line plot uses Xs on a number line to show data.

> Each X represents one child. Since there are 19 Xs, there are 19 children in the group.

Heights of Children

> The shortest child is 46 inches tall.

> The tallest child is 54 inches tall.

> The height of each child is measured in inches.

Height (in inches)

> The line plot shows that there are 19 children, who are between 46 and 54 inches tall.

PRACTICE

Use the line plot to answer the questions.

1. What is the difference in height between the tallest child and the shortest child in the group?

   _____ inches − _____ inches = _____ inches

2. How many children have a height of 48 inches?

   _____ children

Students measure the lengths of some pencils.
Use the line plot of the data to answer Exercises 3–6.

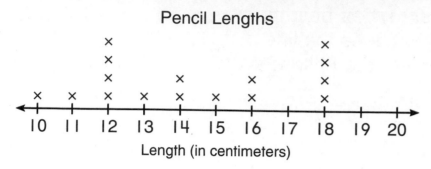

Pencil Lengths

Length (in centimeters)

3. How many pencils are 16 centimeters long
   or greater? _____ pencils

4. How many pencils are shorter than
   14 centimeters? _____ pencils

Problem Solving

5. Bianca says that the most common pencil
   length is 12 cm. Daisy says it is 18 cm.
   Who is correct? Explain.

   _____

   _____

Write About It

6. Sergio says that the students measured
   8 pencils because there are 8 numbers
   with Xs above them. Is he correct? Explain.

   _____

   _____

   _____

Name _____

Read Line Plots

The line plot shows the heights of some children.

Each X represents one child. Since there are 19 Xs, there are 19 children in the group.

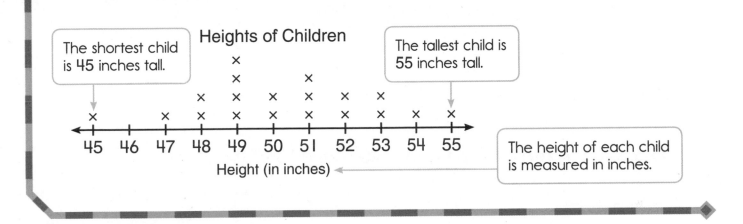

The shortest child is 45 inches tall.

Heights of Children

The tallest child is 55 inches tall.

The height of each child is measured in inches.

Height (in inches)

MORE PRACTICE

Use the line plot about children's heights to answer the questions.

1. What is the difference in height between the tallest child and the shortest child in the group?

   _____ inches − _____ inches = _____ inches

2. How many children have a height of 46 inches?

   _____ children

3. What is the most common height in the group?

   _____

Some children of different ages measured their hand spans. This is the distance from the tip of the pinky finger to the tip of the thumb. Use the line plot of the data to answer Exercises 1–4.

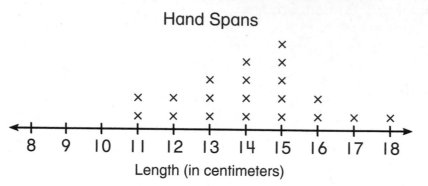

Hand Spans

Length (in centimeters)

1. What is the most common hand span length?

_____

2. How many children measured their hand span?

_____ children

Problem Solving

3. Caitlin's hand span is 2 cm shorter than the most common hand span. What is the length of her hand span?

Caitlin's hand span is _____ centimeters long.

Write About It

4. If another child measures his or her hand span and adds it to the line plot, what length is it *most likely* to be? Explain.

_____

_____

_____

Make Line Plots

Objective
■ Make, read, and interpret line plots.

Math Words
data
tally chart
tally mark
line plot

Donovan measures to the nearest foot the distances that he and 14 classmates can jump. He records the data.

3, 4, 6, 4, 3, 5, 4, 4, 5, 4, 4, 5, 5, 5, 4

How can Donovan display the data?

• First, Donovan can make a tally chart to organize the data.

Jump Distances	
Distance (in feet)	Tally
3	||
4	⊬⊬⊬ ||
5	⊬⊬⊬
6	|

There is one tally mark for each time a distance is jumped.

• Then Donovan can display the data in a line plot.

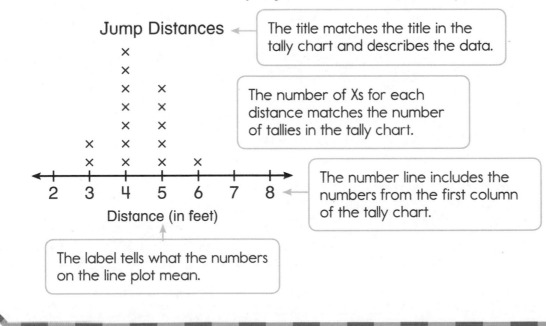

Jump Distances

The title matches the title in the tally chart and describes the data.

The number of Xs for each distance matches the number of tallies in the tally chart.

The number line includes the numbers from the first column of the tally chart.

Distance (in feet)

The label tells what the numbers on the line plot mean.

Use Donovan's line plot to answer Exercises 1–4.

1. Donovan measures the jump of another classmate. This student jumps 5 feet. Describe how Donovan should show this jump on the line plot.

   _____

   _____

2. Another student jumps 2 feet less than the longest jump. Where should Donovan place an X to show this jump on the line plot?

   Donovan should place the X above the number ____.

Problem Solving

3. Donovan's jump distance is 1 foot greater than the most common jump distance. What is his jump distance?

   Donovan's jump distance is ____ feet.

Write About It

4. Explain how you would make a line plot showing the distances your classmates can jump.

   _____

   _____

   _____

   _____

   _____

Name _____

Make Line Plots

This data shows the number of feet 15 students jump.

3, 4, 6, 4, 3, 5, 4, 4, 5, 4, 4, 5, 5, 5, 4

How can you make a line plot of the data?

First, make a tally chart.   Then, show the data.

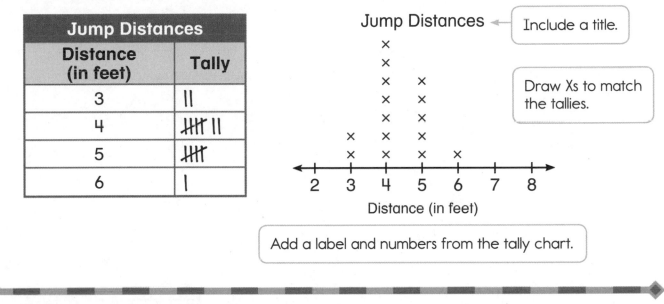

Jump Distances	
Distance (in feet)	Tally
3	II
4	IIII II
5	IIII
6	I

Jump Distances — Include a title.

Draw Xs to match the tallies.

Add a label and numbers from the tally chart.

MORE PRACTICE

A farmer records the heights of 14 plants to the nearest inch: 5, 3, 4, 6, 6, 6, 4, 5, 4, 4, 4, 5, 4, 3

Complete the tally chart and the line plot.

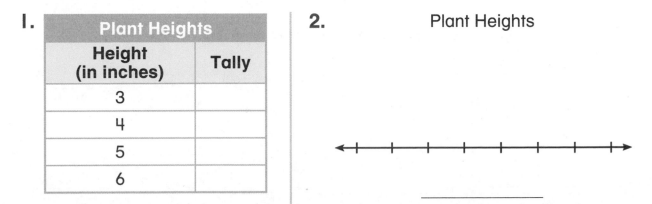

1.

Plant Heights	
Height (in inches)	Tally
3	
4	
5	
6	

2.   Plant Heights

Ben measures and records the lengths
of some library books to the nearest centimeter:
18, 17, 16, 18, 15, 16, 18, 17, 18, 17, 16, 17, 17

Use the data to complete the tally chart.
Then make a line plot of the data.

1.

Library Book Lengths	
Length (in cm)	Tally
15	
16	
17	
18	

2. Library Book Lengths

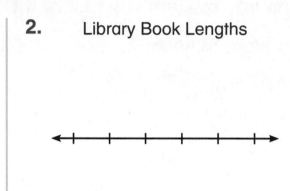

Problem Solving

Use the library book length data to solve.

3. Measure the length of your favorite book to the
    nearest centimeter. How does your book's length
    compare to the most common length in the line plot?

    My book's length is _____

    _____ the most common length in the line plot.

Write About It

4. Why is it helpful to make a tally chart before
    you make a line plot?

    _____

    _____

    _____

Read Picture Graphs

Miranda asks her friends about their favorite type of book. She records the data in a picture graph. What does the picture graph show about Miranda's friends?

Objective
- Read and interpret picture graphs.

Math Words
picture graph
symbol
data
key

A picture graph uses symbols to show data.

Favorite Type of Book	
Fiction	📖 📖 📖 📖 📖 📖 📖 📖
Nonfiction	📖 📖 📖 📖
Key: Each 📖 stands for 1 friend.	

8 friends choose fiction.

4 friends choose nonfiction.

The key tells how many each symbol stands for.

▷ The picture graph shows that 8 friends choose fiction and 4 friends choose nonfiction.

PRACTICE

Use the picture graph about favorite types of books to answer the questions.

1. Which type of book do more friends choose?

   _____

2. How many more friends choose fiction than nonfiction?

   ____ − ____ = ____ friends

The picture graph shows the favorite seasons of a group of students. Use the picture graph to answer the questions.

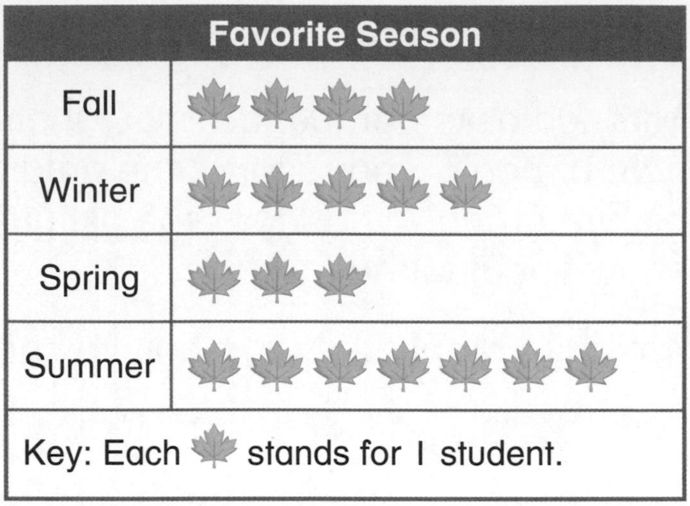

Favorite Season	
Fall	🍁 🍁 🍁 🍁
Winter	🍁 🍁 🍁 🍁 🍁
Spring	🍁 🍁 🍁
Summer	🍁 🍁 🍁 🍁 🍁 🍁 🍁

Key: Each 🍁 stands for 1 student.

3. Which season is the favorite of the least number of students?

_____

4. How many students like spring or summer best?

____ + ____ = ____ students

Problem Solving

Use the picture graph about rainy days to answer the question.

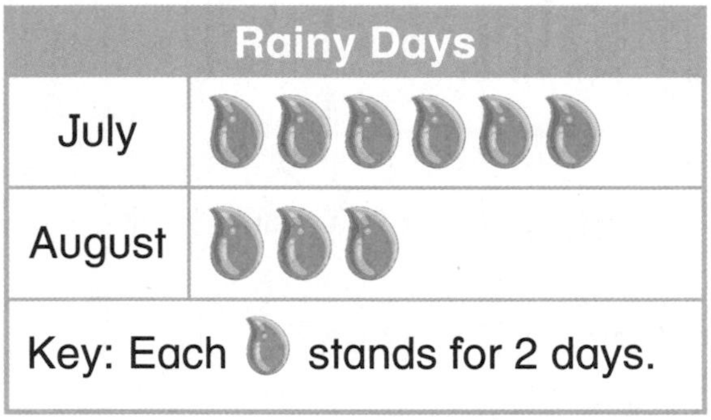

Rainy Days	
July	💧 💧 💧 💧 💧 💧
August	💧 💧 💧

Key: Each 💧 stands for 2 days.

5. How many days did it rain in July and August? Explain how you found your answer.

_____

_____

Write About It

6. Why is it important to read the key before looking at the data in a picture graph?

_____

_____

Read Picture Graphs

This picture graph uses symbols to show data about some friends' favorite types of books.

Favorite Type of Book	
Fiction	📕📕📕📕📕📕📕📕
Nonfiction	📕📕📕📕
Key: Each 📕 stands for 1 friend.	

8 friends choose fiction.

4 friends choose nonfiction.

The key tells how many each symbol stands for.

> The picture graph shows that 8 friends choose fiction and 4 friends choose nonfiction.

MORE PRACTICE

Use the picture graph to answer Exercises 1–3.

Field Trip Location	
Zoo	☺☺☺☺☺☺☺
Museum	☺☺☺☺☺☺☺☺☺
Farm	☺☺☺☺
Key: Each ☺ stands for 1 student.	

1. How many students choose the zoo?

   _____ students

2. Which field trip do the most students vote for?

   _____

3. How many students in all vote?

   ____ + ____ + ____ = ____ students

The picture graph shows the types of pets a group of students have. Use the picture graph to answer Exercises 1–2.

Type of Pet	
Cat	★ ★ ★ ★ ★
Turtle	★ ★ ★ ★ ★ ★ ★
Fish	★ ★
Bird	★ ★ ★ ★
Key: Each ★ stands for 1 student.	

1. Which type of pet do the fewest number of students have?

_____

2. How many more students have a cat than have fish?

_____ − _____ = _____ students

Problem Solving

The picture graph shows the different ways students travel to school. Use the picture graph to answer Exercises 3–4.

Travel to School	
Walk	👣 👣 👣 👣 👣
Car	
Bus	👣 👣 👣 👣 👣 👣 👣 👣
Key: Each 👣 stands for 5 students.	

3. How many students walk or take a bus to school?

_____ students

Write About It

4. If 35 students ride in a car to school, how many symbols should be in that row of the graph? Explain.

_____

_____

_____

Make Picture Graphs

Jeremiah records the number of sunny days for four weeks.

How can Jeremiah make a picture graph of the data?

Sunny Days	
Week	**Tally**
Week 1	~~||||~~	
Week 2	||||
Week 3	|||
Week 4	~~||||~~

Objective
■ Make, read, and interpret picture graphs.

Math Words
tally chart
picture graph
data
symbol
key

Sunny Days	
Week 1	● ● ● ● ● ●
Week 2	● ● ● ●
Week 3	● ● ●
Week 4	● ● ● ● ●
Key: Each ● stands for 1 day.	

First, decide what symbol to use and how many days it will stand for.

Since the symbol stands for 1 day, draw 1 symbol for each sunny day.

Include a key so the reader knows what each symbol means.

The picture graph shows Jeremiah's data.

PRACTICE

Friends voted on their favorite camp activities. Seven chose swimming, 4 chose hiking, 6 chose crafts, and 2 chose music. Use the data to complete the tally chart and picture graph.

1.

Favorite Camp Activity	
Activity	**Tally**
Swimming	~~||||~~ ||
Hiking	
Crafts	
Music	

Favorite Camp Activity	
Swimming	☺ ☺ ☺ ☺ ☺ ☺ ☺
Hiking	
Crafts	
Music	
Key: Each ☺ stands for 1 friend.	

Summer asks her friends to vote on their favorite color. Use the data in the tally chart to complete the picture graph.

2.

Favorite Color	
Color	**Tally**
Red	II
Purple	ЖЖ I
Green	ЖЖ ЖЖ
Blue	ЖЖ I

Favorite Color	

Key: Each ___ stands for I vote.

Problem Solving

Use Summer's data about favorite colors to solve.

3. Summer wants to change her picture graph to use fewer symbols. If she makes each symbol stand for 2 votes, how many symbols will she draw for blue?

   Summer will draw _____ symbols for blue.

Write About It

4. George is making a picture graph to show the number of hits by players in a baseball game. What symbol do you think George should use for the picture graph? Explain.

   _____

   _____

   _____

   _____

Name_____

Make Picture Graphs

This tally chart shows the number of sunny days for four weeks.

How can you make a picture graph of the data?

Sunny Days	
Week	**Tally**
Week 1	ЖΙΙ
Week 2	ΙΙΙΙ
Week 3	ΙΙΙ
Week 4	ЖΙ

> First, decide on the symbol to use and how many days it will stand for.

Sunny Days	
Week 1	⚪ ⚪ ⚪ ⚪ ⚪ ⚪
Week 2	⚪ ⚪ ⚪ ⚪
Week 3	⚪ ⚪ ⚪
Week 4	⚪ ⚪ ⚪ ⚪ ⚪
Key: Each ⚪ stands for 1 day.	

> Since the symbol stands for 1 day, draw 1 symbol for each sunny day.

> Include a key so the reader knows what each symbol means.

MORE PRACTICE

The tally chart shows the sports equipment for a playground.
Use the data to make a picture graph.

Sports Equipment	
Type	**Tally**
Basketball	ЖΙΙ
Soccer Ball	Ж
Football	ΙΙΙ
Kickball	ЖΙΙΙ

1.

Sports Equipment	
Basketball	
Soccer Ball	
Football	
Kickball	
Key: Each ____ stands for 1 ball.	

Hayden records the number of days it snows for three months. It snows 2 days in January, 6 days in February, and 4 days in March. Use Hayden's data to complete the tally chart and picture graph.

1.

Snow Days	
Month	Tally
January	
February	
March	

2.

Snow Days	
Key: Each	stands for ____ day.

Problem Solving

Use Hayden's data about snowy days to solve.

3. It snowed a total of 6 more days last year during the same three months than it snowed this year. How many days did it snow last year?

   It snowed ____ days last year.

Write About It

4. When making a picture graph, why might you decide to use a symbol that stands for more than 1?

   _____

   _____

   _____

Delaney measures pieces of fabric in her dress shop. Use the line plot of the data to answer the questions.

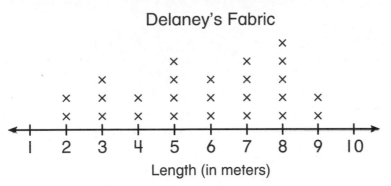

Delaney's Fabric

Length (in meters)

1. How many of Delaney's pieces of fabric have a length of 5 meters or less?

_____ pieces

2. What is the difference in length between the longest and shortest pieces of fabric?

_____

A biologist records the lengths, to the nearest inch, of some frogs' jumps. Use the data in the tally chart to make a line plot.

3.

Frog Jumps	
Length (in inches)	Tally
11	ll
12	ЖГ
13	llll
14	ЖГ l
15	lll
16	l

Frog Jumps

Some students are choosing a name for the class goldfish. The picture graph shows the students' votes. Use the picture graph to answer the questions.

Goldfish Names	
Zippy	🐟 🐟 🐟 🐟 🐟 🐟
Goldie	🐟 🐟 🐟
Frank	🐟 🐟 🐟 🐟 🐟
Key: Each 🐟 stands for 1 vote.	

4. Which name got the fewest votes?

_____

5. If 3 girls voted for Frank, how many boys voted for Frank?

_____ boys

Ling asks her friends about their favorite type of muffin. Use the data in the tally chart to complete the picture graph and answer the question.

6.

Favorite Muffin	
Type	**Tally**
Blueberry	卌
Pumpkin	‖
Banana Nut	‖‖

Favorite Muffin	

7. How many more friends voted for blueberry or banana nut muffins than voted for pumpkin muffins?

_____ friends

Name_____

Read Bar Graphs

Daria makes a bar graph about students in her class. What does her bar graph show?

A bar graph uses bars to show data.

The height of the bar for Wednesday is 8.

The height of the bar for Monday is 7.

The height of the bar for Tuesday is 3.

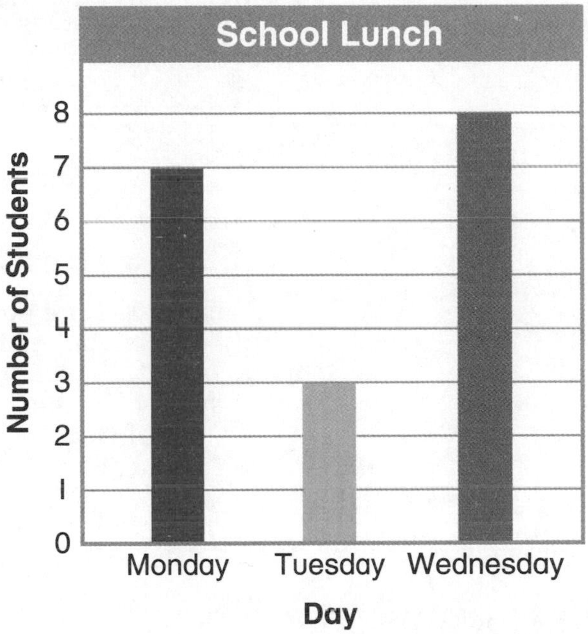

School Lunch

Number of Students

8
7
6
5
4
3
2
1
0

Monday Tuesday Wednesday

Day

Follow the height of the bar across to find the number of students.

➤ The bar graph shows that 7 students eat school lunch on Monday, 3 on Tuesday, and 8 on Wednesday.

PRACTICE

Use Daria's bar graph to answer Exercises 1–2.

1. How many more students eat school lunch on Wednesday than on Tuesday?

   ____ − ____ = ____ students

2. What is the total number of students who eat lunch?

   ____ + ____ + ____ = ____ students

Use the bar graph to answer Exercises 3–5.

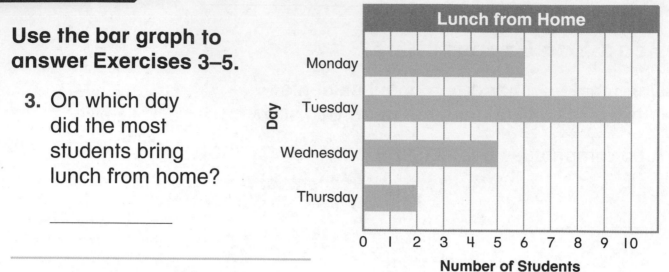

Lunch from Home

Day: Monday, Tuesday, Wednesday, Thursday

Number of Students: 0 1 2 3 4 5 6 7 8 9 10

3. On which day did the most students bring lunch from home?

_____

4. How many more students bring lunch on Wednesday than on Thursday?

_____ students

In this graph, the data is shown in bars that go across. The length of the bar tells the number of students.

Problem Solving

5. How many more students bring lunch on Monday and Tuesday together than on Wednesday and Thursday together?

_____ students

Write About It

6. Some graphs have bars that go up and down. Some have bars that go across. Explain how these graphs are alike and how they are different.

_____

_____

_____

Name_____

Read Bar Graphs

The bar graph uses bars to show data about how many students buy school lunch.

The height of the bar for Wednesday is 8.

The height of the bar for Monday is 7.

The height of the bar for Tuesday is 3.

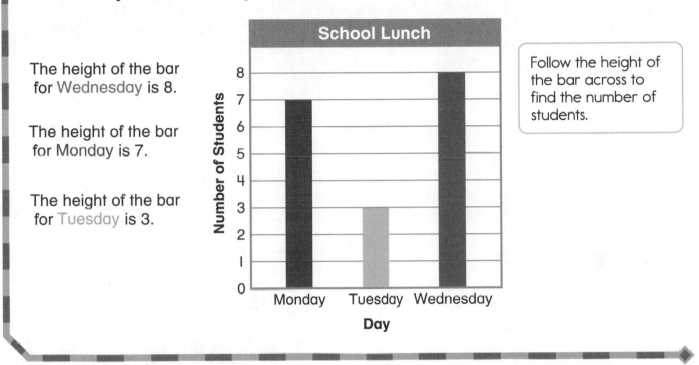

Follow the height of the bar across to find the number of students.

Use the bar graph about after-school activities to answer the questions.

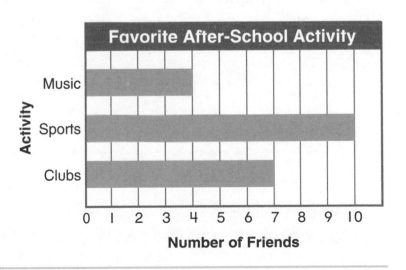

1. Which activity is the favorite of most of the friends?

_____

2. How many friends were asked about their favorite after-school activity?

____ + ____ + ____ = ____ friends

Use the bar graph to answer Exercises 1–2.

1. How many more students take 45 minutes than take 15 minutes to get ready?

   _____ students

2. How many students get ready in less than 45 minutes?

   _____ students

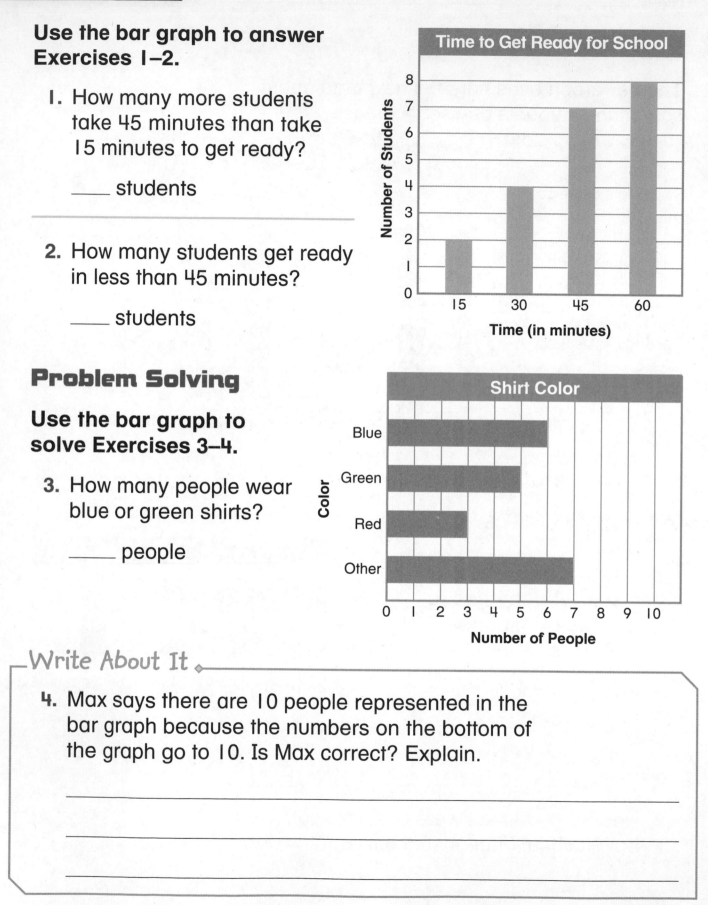

Time to Get Ready for School

Number of Students / Time (in minutes)

Problem Solving

Use the bar graph to solve Exercises 3–4.

3. How many people wear blue or green shirts?

   _____ people

Shirt Color

Color: Blue, Green, Red, Other / Number of People

Write About It

4. Max says there are 10 people represented in the bar graph because the numbers on the bottom of the graph go to 10. Is Max correct? Explain.

_____

_____

_____

Name _____

Make Bar Graphs

Objective
- Make, read, and interpret bar graphs.

Math Words
data
bar graph

Antonio records the types of birds that come to his bird feeder one morning. He shows the data in a tally chart.

Birds at a Bird Feeder	
Bird	**Tally**
Blue Jay	IIII
Chickadee	̶I̶I̶I̶I̶ IIII
Goldfinch	̶I̶I̶I̶I̶ II

How can Antonio make a bar graph of the data?

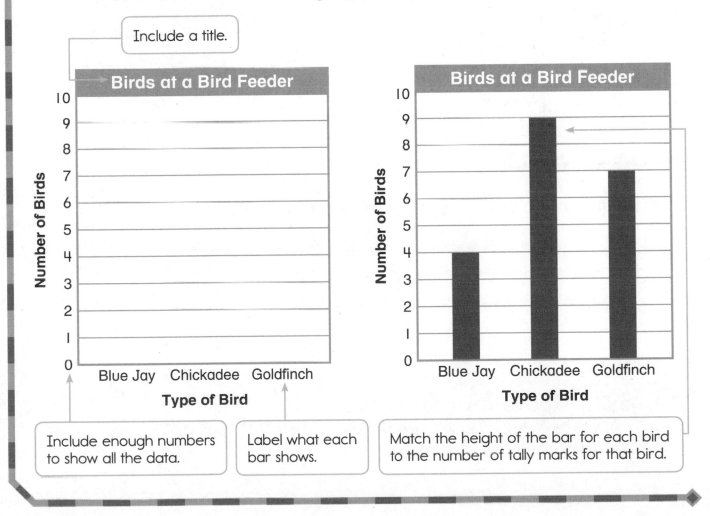

Include a title.

Include enough numbers to show all the data.

Label what each bar shows.

Match the height of the bar for each bird to the number of tally marks for that bird.

A baker records the loaves of bread sold one morning. Use the data in the tally chart to complete the bar graph and answer the question.

1.

Loaves of Bread Sold	
Type	**Tally**
Sourdough	ЖЖ
Wheat	ЖЖ lll
Raisin	lll
Sesame	ЖЖ l

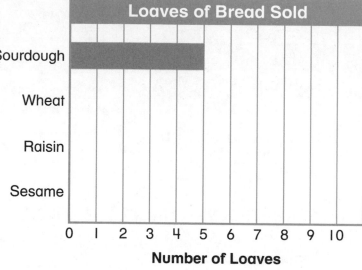

2. How many more loaves of wheat bread are sold than loaves of raisin bread?

_____ loaves

Problem Solving

Use the data about loaves of bread to solve.

3. Later, another 15 loaves of wheat bread are sold, but no more loaves of raisin bread. How many more wheat loaves than raisin loaves are sold now?

_____ more wheat loaves are sold now.

Write About It

4. How do you know how tall or how long to make each bar on a bar graph?

_____

_____

Make Bar Graphs

This tally chart shows the types of birds that visit a bird feeder one morning.

Birds at a Bird Feeder	
Bird	**Tally**
Blue Jay	IIII
Chickadee	ⅢⅡ IIII
Goldfinch	ⅢⅡ II

How can you make a bar graph of the data?

Include a title.

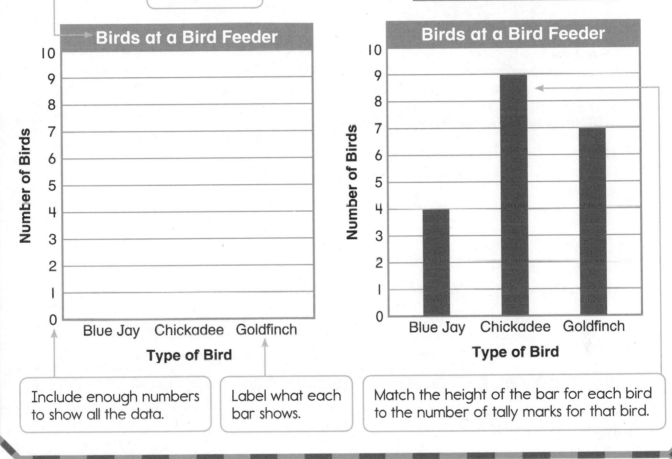

Number of Birds / Birds at a Bird Feeder

Blue Jay   Chickadee   Goldfinch

Type of Bird

Include enough numbers to show all the data.

Label what each bar shows.

Match the height of the bar for each bird to the number of tally marks for that bird.

MORE PRACTICE

Use the data about birds at a bird feeder to answer the question.

1. If 6 sparrows visited the bird feeder, how high would the bar for sparrows reach?

_____

HOMEWORK

Mena records the colors of the fish in her aquarium. Use the data in the tally chart to complete the bar graph and answer the questions.

1.

Fish in Aquarium	
Color	**Tally**
Red	II
Blue	𝍸 II
Yellow	𝍸 III
Orange	IIII

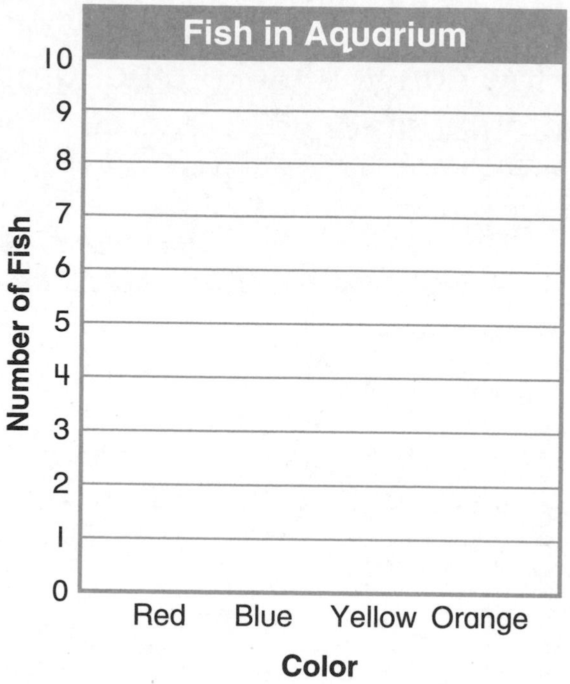

2. How many more red and yellow fish are there than orange fish?

____ fish

Problem Solving

Use the data about Mena's fish to solve.

3. Mena wants to add enough red fish to the aquarium so that she has 2 more red fish than yellow fish. How many red fish does she need to add?

Mena needs to add ____ red fish.

Write About It

4. Does it matter if you draw a bar graph that has bars going up and down or bars that go across? Explain.

____

____

____

Name _____

Problem Solving ⟩Read⟩ ⟩Plan⟩ ⟩Solve⟩ ⟩Check⟩
Choose A Model

Objective
- Choose a model to organize data for a given problem-solving situation.

Math Words
data
model
picture graph
bar graph
line plot

Lindsey asks some students which activity they want to have for field day.

What type of model should Lindsey use to show her data? Which two activities should be part of field day?

Field Day	
Activity	**Tally**
Relay Races	卌 III
Kickball	卌 卌 II
Face Painting	卌
Capture the Flag	卌 卌 IIII

There are four categories of data.

Each category has a count.

A line plot would be the best model to show numerical data, such as heights or lengths.

- First, think about the type of data.

- Then, choose a model and draw it. A picture graph or bar graph is the best model to show counts of different categories of data.

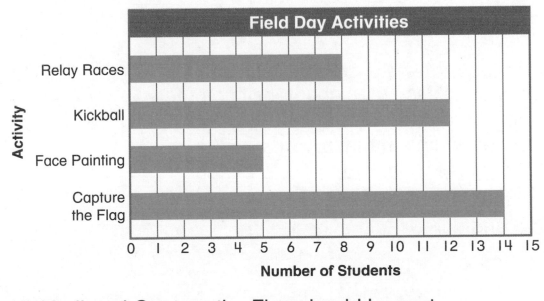

Field Day Activities

Activity / Number of Students

Kickball and Capture the Flag should be part of field day because they have the most votes.

Read and solve the problem.

1. Omar measures, to the nearest inch,
   the length of each shell in his collection.

   5, 2, 3, 3, 5, 2, 6, 3, 2, 5, 6, 3, 5, 3

   What length of shell is the most common?

   Make a model that best displays the data.
   Use your model to answer the question.

   The most common length of shell is _____.

Write About It

2. Katie asks her classmates about their favorite
   subject. She records the number of students
   who choose reading, math, art, or music.
   Should Katie use a bar graph, picture graph,
   or line plot to model the data? Explain.

   _____

   _____

   _____

Name _____

Problem Solving
Choose A Model

A carnival game has each player rolling a ball toward a target. The distance, in inches, from the ball to the target after the roll for 12 players is shown.

4, 6, 8, 5, 7, 6, 8, 5, 6, 8, 6, 5

Players win a prize if the distance is less than 7 inches. How many players win a prize?

- Think about the type of data.

- Choose a model and draw it.

> The data is numerical. It is a set of lengths. So, a line plot is best.

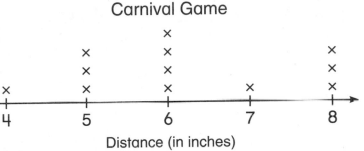

Carnival Game

Distance (in inches)

There are 8 players whose ball was less than 7 inches from the target after the roll.

▷ Eight players win a prize.

Use the line plot about the carnival game to answer the question.

1. Brady's roll was 3 inches farther from the target than the greatest distance on the line plot. How far was Brady's roll from the target?

   Brady's roll was _____ inches from the target.

Choose a bar graph, picture graph, or line plot to help solve the problems.

2. Marissa asks her friends about their favorite flavor of yogurt.
The tally chart shows the data.

Draw a model of the data.

Favorite Yogurt Flavor	
Flavor	**Tally**
Strawberry	IIII
Blueberry	II
Lemon	III
Vanilla	IIII

3. Marissa wants to make a smoothie with the two most popular flavors. Which flavors should she use?

Marissa should use _____ and

_____ yogurt flavors.

4. Nolan's favorite yogurt flavor is picked 2 fewer times than vanilla. What is Nolan's favorite yogurt flavor?

Nolan's favorite yogurt flavor is _____.

HOMEWORK

Read and solve each problem.

1. At a trivia contest there are four rounds. A team's final score is the total of their three highest-scoring rounds. What is this team's final score?

   The final score is _____ points.

Trivia Contest	
Round	**Score**
1	215
2	149
3	320
4	282

Use the data in the tally chart for Exercises 2–4.

2. The students in an art class vote for their choice for next project.

   Choose a bar graph, picture graph, or line plot. Draw a model of the data.

Next Art Project	
Project	**Tally**
Pottery	ЖІ І
Painting	‖
Drawing	ЖІ

3. How many students vote?

   _____ students

4. Al votes for the project that has 4 fewer votes than the most popular project. What was Al's vote?

   Al votes for _____.

Choose a bar graph, picture graph, or line plot to help you solve the problem.

5. Jayla measures, to the nearest foot, the lengths of some jump ropes.

   7, 9, 8, 9, 8, 7, 10, 7, 7, 9

   How many more jump ropes are 7 feet long than 10 feet long?

   Draw a model of the data.

   There are _____ more 7-foot-long jump ropes than 10-foot-long jump ropes.

Write About It

6. Two of Clark's friends have blonde hair, 4 have brown, 3 have black, and 2 have red hair. Should Clark use a bar graph, picture graph, or line plot to model the data? Explain.

   _____

   _____

   _____

A group of students measures the lengths of some colored pencils in the classroom. Use the data in the tally chart to make a line plot and answer the question.

1.

Colored Pencil Lengths	
Length (in cm)	**Tally**
12	JHT II
13	IIII
14	III
15	JHT
16	III
17	I

2. How many colored pencils have a length greater than 14 centimeters?

_____ colored pencils

Rex asks his friends what type of school show they would most like to see next spring. Use the data in the tally chart to complete the picture graph.

3.

Spring Show	
Type	**Tally**
Play	JHT II
Musical	III
Talent Show	JHT I

Spring Show	

Key: Each ___ stands for 1 vote.

A gym teacher asks some students about their favorite sport. The tally chart shows the data. Use the data to complete the bar graph and answer the questions.

4.

Favorite Sport	
Sport	**Tally**
Football	卌 卌 IIII
Baseball	卌 卌 I
Soccer	卌 I
Basketball	卌 II

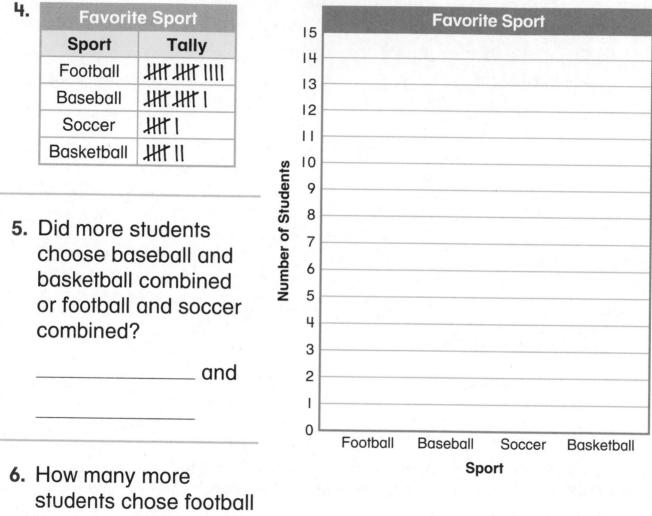

Favorite Sport

Number of Students — Sport: Football, Baseball, Soccer, Basketball

5. Did more students choose baseball and basketball combined or football and soccer combined?

_____ and

_____

6. How many more students chose football than chose basketball?

_____ students

7. Football received more votes than which two sports combined?

_____ and _____

CHAPTER 11 Review

Name _____

The tally chart shows the number of objects made from recyclable materials found in 50 pounds of trash.

Recyclable Materials in Trash	
Material	**Number of objects**
Plastic	ЖІ ІІ
Metal	ІІІ
Paper	ЖІ ЖІ ІІІ
Glass	І

1. Make a bar graph to model the data.

2. How many objects made from recyclable materials were found in the trash in all?

   _____

3. Work with a partner to make up your own data showing the number of recyclable materials found in the trash in your class.

   • Make a tally chart to organize your data.
   • Make a bar graph or picture graph to model your data.
   • Ask and answer at least three questions about your data.

CHAPTER II
Fluency Practice

Name _____

Determine the best answer for each problem.

1. Which is the expanded form of 329?

   A. 3 + 2 + 9

   B. 30 + 2 + 9

   C. 300 + 20 + 9

   D. 300 + 20 + 90

2. Add.

$$\begin{array}{r} 157 \\ +286 \\ \hline \end{array}$$

3. Which three answers have a difference less than 100?

   A. 351 − 236

   B. 504 − 415

   C. 755 − 562

   D. 884 − 791

   E. 927 − 850

4. Write an equation for the array to show how many in all.

   × × × × ×

   × × × × ×

   × × × × ×

   _____

   _____

5. Subtract.

$$\begin{array}{r} 372 \\ -157 \\ \hline \end{array}$$

6. Write 703 in expanded form.

   _____

7. What is the value of the digit 8 in 381?

   _____

8. What is the value of the digit 9 in 954?

   _____

9. Use mental math to add.

   157 + 50 = _____

10. Use mental math to subtract.

   408 − 20 = _____

Money and Time

The United States Mint is the place that makes our coins, from pennies to dollar coins.

Have you seen your state's quarter? Quarters all used to look the same, but now they can look different.

Coin Designs

♦ The State Quarters program has 50 designs—one for each state.

♦ The America the Beautiful Quarters program honors our national parks.

♦ The quarter now has over 100 designs!

Start a Collection

♦ Look for coins with special designs.

♦ Compare coin designs. Which is is your favorite? Why?

Dear Family,

In this chapter, we will be learning about money and time.

Here are some key **Math** Words for this chapter:

penny	**hour hand**
nickel	**minute hand**
dime	**half hour**
quarter	**half past**
change	**A.M.**
dollar sign	**P.M.**

You can use the glossary to find the definition of each word and help your child make flash cards to study each day we work on the lessons in the chapter.

During this chapter about money and time, we will also be making STEAM (Science, Technology, Engineering, the Arts, and Mathematics) connections about coins and design. Read the opening to the chapter together.

Keep Your Skills Sharp

Here is a **Keep Your Skills Sharp** activity to do at home to prepare for this chapter.

Give your child a collection of coins. Have your child identify the name and value of each coin. Encourage your child to describe the coins. Challenge him or her to count the value of a group of two or three coins.

Name _____

Pennies, Nickels, and Dimes

Aaron finds these coins in his pocket.

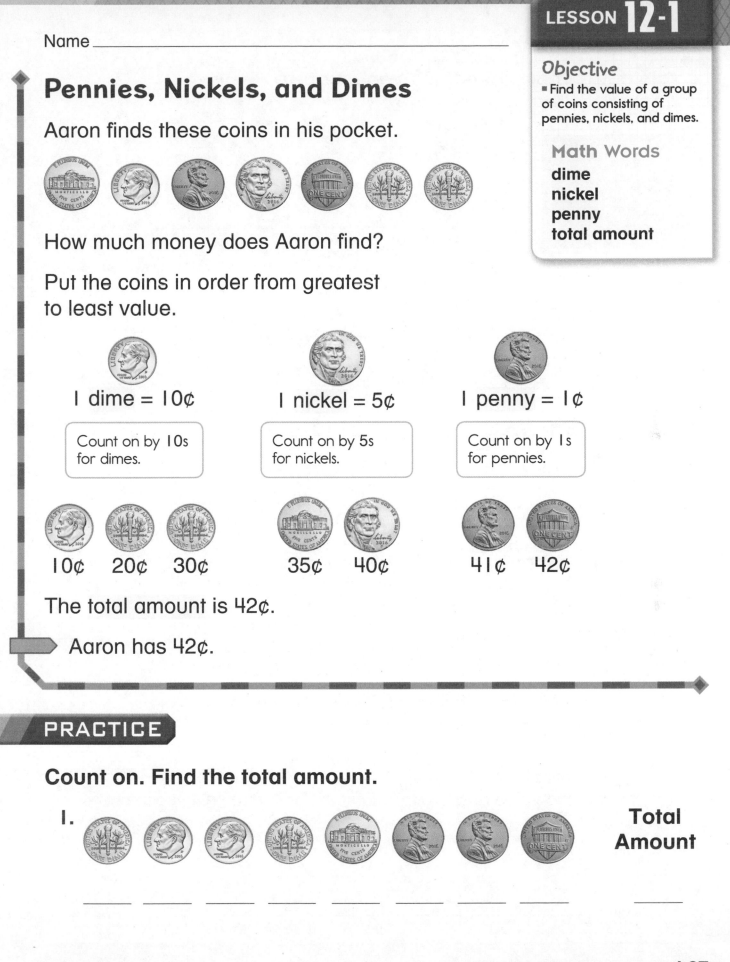

Objective
▪ Find the value of a group of coins consisting of pennies, nickels, and dimes.

Math Words
dime
nickel
penny
total amount

How much money does Aaron find?

Put the coins in order from greatest to least value.

I dime = 10¢   I nickel = 5¢   I penny = 1¢

Count on by 10s for dimes.   Count on by 5s for nickels.   Count on by 1s for pennies.

10¢ 20¢ 30¢   35¢ 40¢   41¢ 42¢

The total amount is 42¢.

Aaron has 42¢.

PRACTICE

Count on. Find the total amount.

1.

Total Amount

_____ _____ _____ _____ _____ _____ _____ _____   _____

Circle coins that make the given amount.

2. 35¢

3. 52¢

4. 40¢

Problem Solving

Count on to solve.

5. Camilla has 52¢ in her wallet. She finds
2 dimes and 9 pennies in her pocket.
How much money does Camilla have in all?

Camilla has _____ ¢ in all.

┌─ Write About It ◆───────────────────────────

6. How does sorting like coins and then ordering
them from greatest to least value help you find
the total amount?

_____

_____

_____

_____

Name_____

Pennies, Nickels, And Dimes

Find the total amount of the group of coins.

Put the coins in order from greatest to least value.

| 1 dime = 10¢ | 1 nickel = 5¢ | 1 penny = 1¢ |
| Count on by 10s. | Count on by 5s. | Count on by 1s. |

10¢   20¢   30¢   35¢   40¢   41¢   42¢

The total amount is 42¢.

MORE PRACTICE

Count on. Find the total amount.

Total Amount

1. 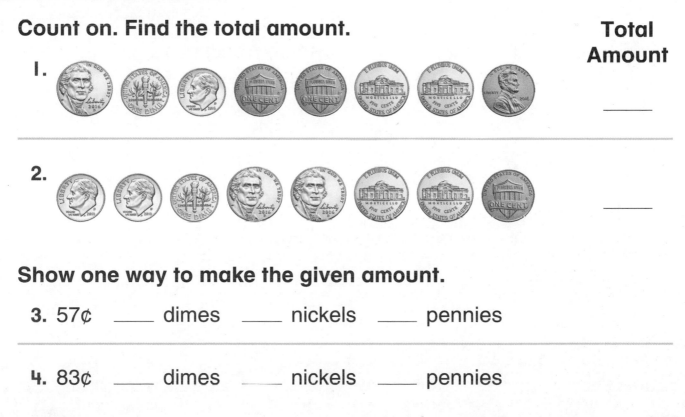   _____

2.   _____

Show one way to make the given amount.

3. 57¢ _____ dimes _____ nickels _____ pennies

4. 83¢ _____ dimes _____ nickels _____ pennies

Circle coins that make the given amount.

1. 18¢

2. 31¢

Match the coins to the total amount.

3. 7 dimes and 3 pennies   **A.** 49¢

4. 4 dimes, 1 nickel, and 4 pennies   **B.** 73¢

5. 3 dimes, 1 nickel, and 3 pennies   **C.** 38¢

Problem Solving

Count on to solve.

6. Justin has 30¢. He finds two coins in his backpack. Now he has 45¢. What two coins does Justin find?

 Justin finds a _____ and a _____.

Write About It

7. Malachi has 6 nickels and 2 dimes. Noah has 5 dimes. Who has more money? Explain.

 _____

 _____

 _____

Name _____

Quarters

Math Words
quarter
penny
nickel
dime

Naomi buys a ruler using the coins shown.

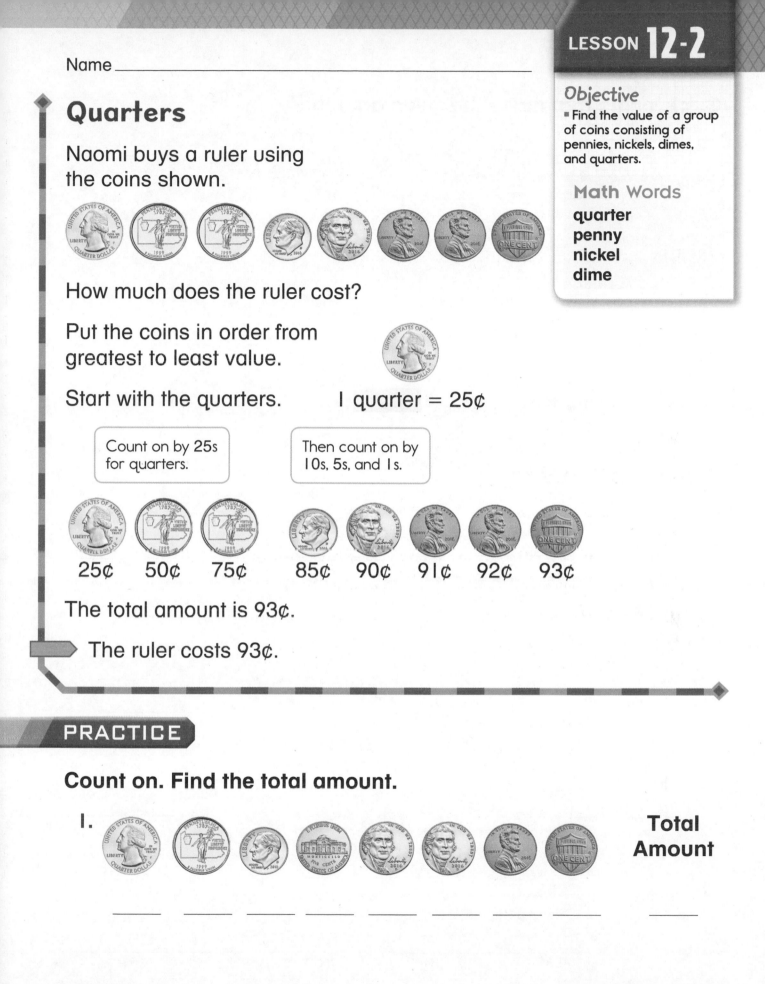

How much does the ruler cost?

Put the coins in order from greatest to least value.

Start with the quarters.   1 quarter = 25¢

Count on by 25s for quarters.   Then count on by 10s, 5s, and 1s.

25¢   50¢   75¢   85¢   90¢   91¢   92¢   93¢

The total amount is 93¢.

The ruler costs 93¢.

PRACTICE

Count on. Find the total amount.

1.

Total Amount

___ ___ ___ ___ ___ ___ ___ ___

Circle coins that make the given amount.

2. 62¢

3. 48¢

4. 32¢

Problem Solving

Count on to solve.

5. Sabrina has 1 quarter, 1 dime, and 4 pennies.
   She has 50¢ less than Kylie. How much money
   does Kylie have?

   Kylie has _____¢.

Write About It

6. Timothy has 3 coins that have a total value of 40¢.
   What coins does Timothy have? Explain.

   _____

   _____

   _____

   _____

Name _____

Quarters

Find the total amount of the group of coins.

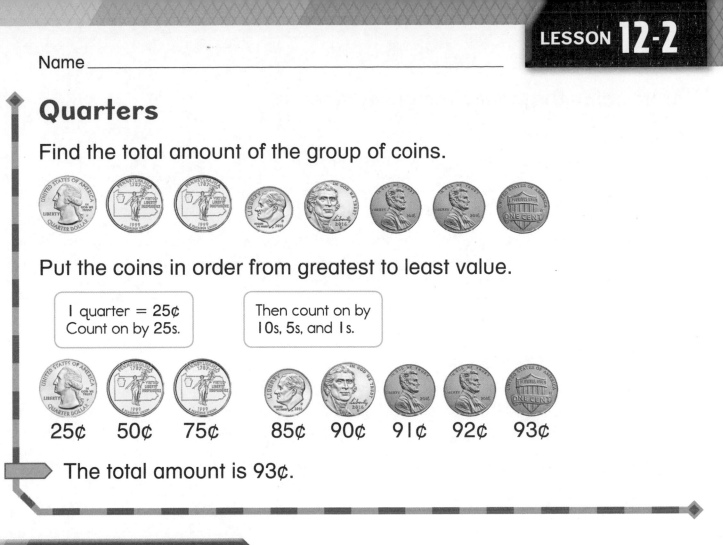

Put the coins in order from greatest to least value.

| I quarter = 25¢
Count on by 25s. | Then count on by
10s, 5s, and 1s. |

25¢   50¢   75¢   85¢   90¢   91¢   92¢   93¢

▷ The total amount is 93¢.

MORE PRACTICE

Find the total amount.

Total Amount

1.

_____

2. What is another way to show the total amount?

_____

Show one way to make the given amount.

3. 62¢ ____ quarters ____ dimes ____ nickels ____ pennies

4. 94¢ ____ quarters ____ dimes ____ nickels ____ pennies

Circle coins that make the given amount.

1. 37¢

2. 82¢

Problem Solving

Count on to solve.

3. Daniela uses 4 dimes, 2 quarters, and 3 pennies to buy a snack. How much does the snack cost?

   The snack costs _____¢.

4. Jordan has 55¢. He finds two coins on his desk. Now he has 81¢. What two coins does Jordan find?

   Jordan finds a _____ and a _____.

Write About It

5. Stella has 4 dimes, 7 nickels, and 2 pennies. Rae has 3 quarters and 1 nickel. Stella says her coins are worth more because she has more coins. Is Stella correct? Explain.

   _____

   _____

   _____

Equal Amounts

Gregory and Damian have the coins shown.

Gregory   Damian

Do the boys have equal amounts of money?

Equal amounts have the same value.

Find the amount of money for each boy.

Arrange the coins in order from greatest value to least value.

Count on to find the total amount in each group.

Gregory

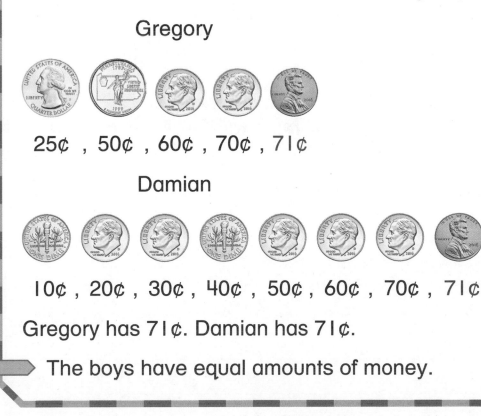

25¢ , 50¢ , 60¢ , 70¢ , 71¢

Damian

10¢ , 20¢ , 30¢ , 40¢ , 50¢ , 60¢ , 70¢ , 71¢

Gregory has 71¢. Damian has 71¢.

> The boys have equal amounts of money.

Circle Yes or No to tell if the groups of coins show equal amounts.

1.

Yes

No

Show two ways to make each amount.

2. 82¢

____ ____ ____ ____

____ ____ ____ ____

3. 43¢

____ ____ ____ ____

____ ____ ____ ____

Problem Solving

4. Layla has 6 dimes and 3 nickels. Audrey has 2 quarters. What coin does Audrey need for the girls to have equal amounts?

Audrey needs a _____.

Write About It

5. How can you find out if two groups of coins show equal amounts?

_____

_____

Name _____

Equal Amounts

A group of coins has 2 quarters, 2 dimes, and 1 penny. Another group of coins has 7 dimes and 1 penny. Do the groups of coins have equal amounts?

Find the amount for each group of coins.

Arrange the coins in order from greatest value to least value. Then count on.

25¢ , 50¢ , 60¢ , 70¢ , 71¢

10¢ , 20¢ , 30¢ , 40¢ , 50¢ , 60¢ , 70¢ , 71¢

> Both groups of coins have 71¢.
> They have equal amounts.

MORE PRACTICE

Show three ways to make each amount.

1. 59¢

___ ___ ___ ___

___ ___ ___ ___

___ ___ ___ ___

2. 71¢

___ ___ ___ ___

___ ___ ___ ___

___ ___ ___ ___

Show three ways to make each amount.

1. 38¢

2. 80¢

_____ _____ _____ _____   _____ _____ _____ _____

_____ _____ _____ _____   _____ _____ _____ _____

_____ _____ _____ _____   _____ _____ _____ _____

Match the sets of coins with equal amounts.

3. 7 dimes and 2 nickels

4. 2 quarters and 3 nickels

5. 3 quarters and 1 dime

A. 7 dimes and 3 nickels

B. 3 quarters and 1 nickel

C. 6 dimes and 1 nickel

Problem Solving

6. Liam has 5 nickels. Art has 3 dimes and 1 nickel.
   What coin does Liam need to have an equal amount?

   Liam needs a _____.

Write About It

7. Ava has 2 quarters and 5 pennies. Mia has 5 dimes
   and 3 nickels. Which coin should Mia give Ava so
   they have equal amounts? Explain.

   _____

   _____

Name _____

Compare Money

At a farmers' market, Haley wants to buy a mango for 93¢. She has the money shown. Does Haley have enough money to buy the mango?

Objective
▪ Compare an amount of money to the cost of an item.

Math Words
compare
penny
nickel
dime
quarter

- First, find the total amount of Haley's money.

25¢   50¢   75¢   85¢ 95¢ 96¢ 97¢ 98¢

- Then, compare the total amount to the cost of the mango.

98¢ is greater than 93¢.

Haley has enough money to buy the mango.

PRACTICE

Write the total amount. Then, write *yes* or *no* to tell if it is enough money to buy the item.

1.

 56¢

Is there enough money?

_____   _____

Write which piece of fruit you can buy with the coins shown.

Farmers' Market Prices	
Mango	93¢
Orange	56¢
Lemon	39¢
Pear	84¢

2.

_____

3.

_____

Problem Solving

Use the Farmers' Market Prices chart to solve.

4. Evan wants to buy a pear. He has 6 dimes, 3 nickels, and 2 pennies. He needs one more coin to be able to buy the pear. What coin does Evan need?

   Evan needs a _____.

Write About It

5. Joe has 2 quarters, 3 dimes, and 1 nickel. He wants to know if he has enough money to buy a lemon. Explain why he does not need to find the total amount of money to decide.

   _____

   _____

   _____

Name_____

Compare Money

Can Haley buy a mango for 93¢ using the money shown?

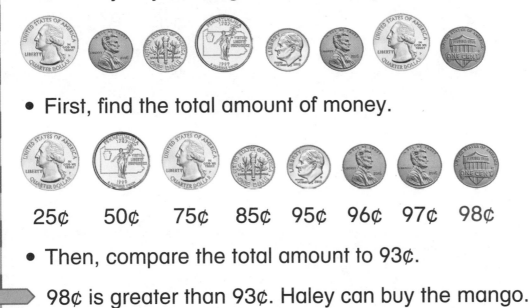

- First, find the total amount of money.

| 25¢ | 50¢ | 75¢ | 85¢ | 95¢ | 96¢ | 97¢ | 98¢ |

- Then, compare the total amount to 93¢.

➤ 98¢ is greater than 93¢. Haley can buy the mango.

MORE PRACTICE

Write the total amount. Then write *yes* or *no* to tell if it is enough money to buy the item.

1. A folder costs 88¢.

 _____

Is there enough money? _____

2. An eraser costs 51¢.

 _____

Is there enough money? _____

Compare the total amounts of the two groups of
coins. Circle the group with the greater amount.

1.

Problem Solving

2. Regan wants to buy a pencil for 47¢.
She has 1 quarter, 1 dime, and 5 pennies.
Does Regan need a nickel or a dime more
to have enough money to buy the pencil?

Regan needs a _____ .

3. Emmanuel buys an eraser for 36¢. He pays
the exact amount with 3 different coins. Which coins
could Emmanuel use to pay for the eraser?

Emmanuel could use _____ .

Write About It

4. A snack costs 83¢. Can you buy that snack with
1 quarter, 3 dimes, 5 nickels, and 2 pennies? Explain.

_____

_____

_____

Name _____

Make Change

George buys a toy car for 47¢. He pays for the car with 2 quarters. How much change does George receive?

- First, find the amount that George paid.

25¢   50¢   2 quarters is 50¢.

- Then find the amount of change, or money back, that George receives.

Count up from the price to the amount paid.
Count up by 1s from 47¢ to 50¢.

48¢   49¢   50¢

➤ George receives 3¢ change.

Objective
- Find the amount of change needed, given the price and amount paid.

Math Words
change
quarter
dime
nickel
penny

PRACTICE

Find the amount paid. Then find the change.

Price	Amount Paid	Change
1. 17¢		____ ____
2. 33¢		____ ____

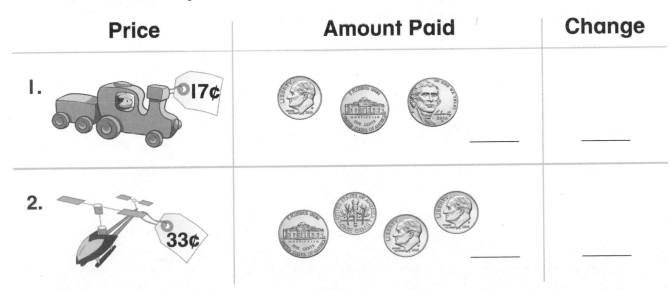

**Two friends each buy a toy truck for 68¢.
How much change will each friend receive?**

3. Melissa uses

Her change is _____.

4. Erin uses

Her change is _____.

Problem Solving

5. Kyle wants to buy a toy plane for 89¢.
He has 3 quarters. His mother gives
him 2 dimes. How much change will
Kyle receive?

Kyle will receive _____¢ change.

Write About It

6. How do you decide how much change
someone receives?

_____

_____

_____

_____

Name _____

Make Change

A toy car costs 47¢. Find the change you receive if you pay for the car with 2 quarters.

- First, find the amount paid.

25¢   50¢   2 quarters is 50¢.

- Then find the amount of change, or money back.

Count up from the price to the amount paid. Count up by 1s from 47¢ to 50¢.

48¢   49¢   50¢

The change is 3¢.

MORE PRACTICE

Find the amount paid. Then find the change.

Price	Amount Paid	Change
1. 41¢		____ ____
2. 72¢		____ ____

A glow stick costs 39¢. The coins show the amount paid. Write the amount of change.

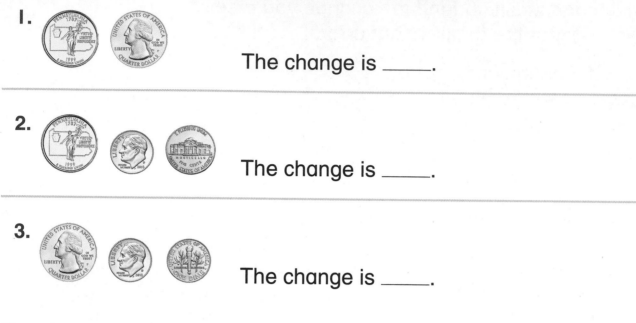

I. The change is _____.

2. The change is _____.

3. The change is _____.

Problem Solving

4. Mason wants to buy either a pinwheel for 68¢ or a yo-yo for 77¢. He has 2 quarters, 2 dimes, and I nickel. Which item can Mason buy? How much change will he receive?

Mason can buy the _____.

He will receive _____¢ change.

Write About It

5. Explain how you decided which item Mason can buy and how much change he will receive.

_____

_____

_____

Name_____

Add and Subtract Money

Objective
- Add and subtract amounts of money.

Math Words

sum
difference
dimes
pennies

Zoe has 56¢. Erin has 38¢. How much money do the girls have in all? What is the difference of the amounts they have?

First, find the sum of the amounts.

dimes	pennies
1	
5	6¢
+ 3	8¢
9	4¢

> Add the pennies first.
> There are more than 9 pennies.
> Regroup 10 pennies as 1 dime.
> Then add the dimes.

Zoe and Erin have 94¢ in all.

Then, find the difference of the amounts.

dimes	pennies
4	16
5	6¢
− 3	8¢
1	8¢

> Subtract the pennies first.
> There are not enough pennies to subtract.
> Regroup 1 dime as 10 pennies.
> Then subtract.

> When you add and subtract cents, think of the pennies as ones and the dimes as tens.

The difference of the amounts they have is 18¢.

PRACTICE

Find the sum or difference. Regroup where needed.

1.

dimes	pennies
2	9¢
+	7¢
	¢

2.

dimes	pennies
4	0¢
− 2	7¢
	¢

Find the sum or difference. Regroup where needed.

3.

	8	5¢
−	4	6¢
		¢

4.

	4	1¢
+	2	9¢
		¢

5.

	5	1¢
−	1	9¢
		¢

6. 88¢ + 5¢ = _____

7. 93¢ − 57¢ = _____

Find the total cost to buy each set of items.

62¢   18¢   29¢   55¢

8. crayons and pencil _____

9. scissors and glue _____

Problem Solving

10. Peter buys a roll of tape for 39¢ and a pen for 28¢. He pays 75¢. How much change does Peter receive?

    Peter receives _____¢ change.

Write About It

11. How is adding dimes and pennies like adding tens and ones?

    _____

    _____

Name_____

Add and Subtract Money

Find the sum of 56¢ and 38¢.

dimes	pennies
I	
5	6¢
+ 3	8¢
9	4¢

> Add the pennies first.
> There are more than 9 pennies.
> Regroup 10 pennies as 1 dime.
> Then add the dimes.

➤ The sum is 94¢.

Find the difference of 56¢ and 38¢.

dimes	pennies
4	16
5	6̶¢
− 3	8¢
I	8¢

> Subtract the pennies first.
> There are not enough pennies to subtract.
> Regroup 1 dime as 10 pennies.
> Then subtract.

➤ The difference is 18¢.

MORE PRACTICE

Find the sum or difference. Regroup where needed.

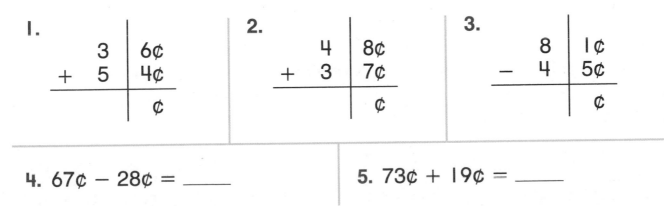

1.
3	6¢
+ 5	4¢
	¢

2.
4	8¢
+ 3	7¢
	¢

3.
8	1¢
− 4	5¢
	¢

4. 67¢ − 28¢ = _____

5. 73¢ + 19¢ = _____

Find the total cost of each set of toys.

 39¢  28¢  54¢  35¢

1. a sailboat and a car

_____

2. 2 sailboats and a spaceship

_____

3. How much more is a robot than a spaceship?   _____

4. How much more is a car than a sailboat?   _____

Problem Solving

Use the prices from the toy sale to solve.

5. Preston has 50¢. He buys a toy and receives 22¢ change. What toy does Preston buy?

Preston buys a _____.

─Write About It

6. Claire has 50¢. She wants to buy 2 sailboats from the toy sale. How can you use mental math to decide if she has enough money?

_____

_____

Name_____

One Dollar

Kaden has a one-dollar bill.
Julian has 4 quarters.
What is each boy's total amount?

First, find the Kaden's amount.

A one-dollar bill is
equal to 100¢.

To write one dollar, use a dollar sign to the left
of the amount.

Kaden has $1, or 100¢.

Now, find Julian's amount.

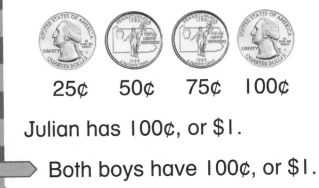

   25¢   50¢   75¢   100¢

Julian has 100¢, or $1.

> Both boys have 100¢, or $1.

Objective
■ Count and find amounts
of coins equal to a dollar.

Math Words
**one-dollar bill
dollar sign**

PRACTICE

Count on. Find the total amount.

1.

**Total
Amount**

_____

Circle groups of coins equal to $1. Draw an X through groups of coins not equal to $1.

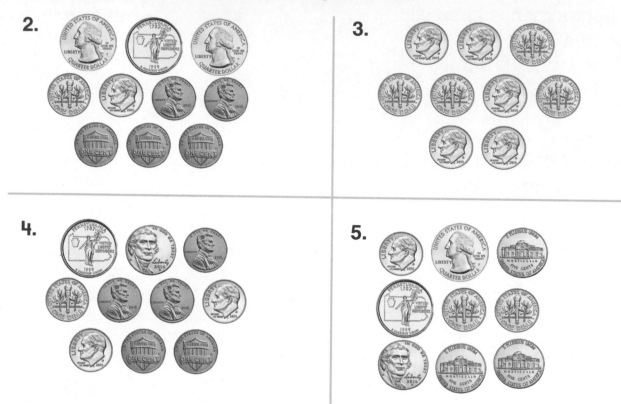

2.

3.

4.

5.

Problem Solving

6. Levi has 18¢ and his brother has 26¢. How much more do the boys need to have a total amount of $1?

   The boys need _____¢ more.

─Write About It ◈───────────────────

7. Jackson has a group of dimes that is equal to $1. How many dimes does Jackson have? Explain.

   _____

   _____

Name _____

One Dollar

A one-dollar bill is equal to 100¢.

To write one dollar, use the dollar sign, $,
to the left of the amount.

$1 = 100¢

4 quarters equal 100¢.

25¢   50¢   75¢   100¢

100¢ in coins can also be written as $1.

MORE PRACTICE

**Circle the group of coins equal to $1. Draw an X
through the group of coins not equal to $1.**

1.

2.

Circle coins to make $1.

1.

2.

Show three ways to make $1.

3. _____ quarters   _____ dimes   _____ nickels   _____ pennies

   _____ quarters   _____ dimes   _____ nickels   _____ pennies

   _____ quarters   _____ dimes   _____ nickels   _____ pennies

Problem Solving

4. Amy has some coins. Shanti has 37¢. Together the girls have $1. How much money does Amy have?

   Amy has _____¢.

Write About It

5. Nora has a group of nickels that is equal to $1. How many nickels does Nora have? Explain.

   _____

   _____

   _____

Name_____

Paper Money

Objective
- Find the value of a group of bills.

Math Words

one-dollar bill
five-dollar bill
ten-dollar bill
twenty-dollar bill
fifty-dollar bill
one hundred-dollar bill

A bank has a display of paper money.

What is the total amount shown in the display?

- First, find the value of each bill.

one-dollar bill = $1   five-dollar bill = $5   ten-dollar bill = $10

 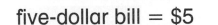

twenty-dollar bill = $20   fifty-dollar bill = $50

one hundred-dollar bill = $100

- Then add the bills in order from greatest value to least value.

$100 + $50 + $20 + $10 + $5 + $1 = $186

The total amount in the bank display is $186.

Count on. Find the total amount.

1. _____

2. _____

3. _____

4. Conner buys a baseball glove. He pays with a one hundred-dollar bill and receives $43 in change. How much does the baseball glove cost?

   The baseball glove costs $ _____.

Write About It

5. How do you find the total amount of a group of bills?

_____

_____

_____

_____

Name _____

Paper Money

Find the total amount shown in the display.

First, find the value of each bill.
Next, Arrange in order. Then add.

one-dollar bill = $1   five-dollar bill = $5   ten-dollar bill = $10

twenty-dollar bill   fifty-dollar bill   one hundred-
= $20   = $50   dollar bill = $100

$100 + $50 + $20 + $10 + $5 + $1 = $186

MORE PRACTICE

Find the total amount.

1.

_____

Compare the total amounts of the two groups of bills. Circle the group with the greater amount.

1.

Show the amount in two ways.

2. $207

_____ _____ _____ _____ _____ _____

_____ _____ _____ _____ _____ _____

Problem Solving

3. Lucas wants to buy a watch for $73. He has $54. How much more money does Lucas need to buy the watch?

   Lucas needs $ _____ more to buy the watch.

Write About It

4. Jacob buys a toy for $16. He pays with one $10 bill and two $5 bills. The cashier gives him $14 in change. Explain what the cashier did wrong.

   _____

   _____

Name_____

Find the total amount.

1.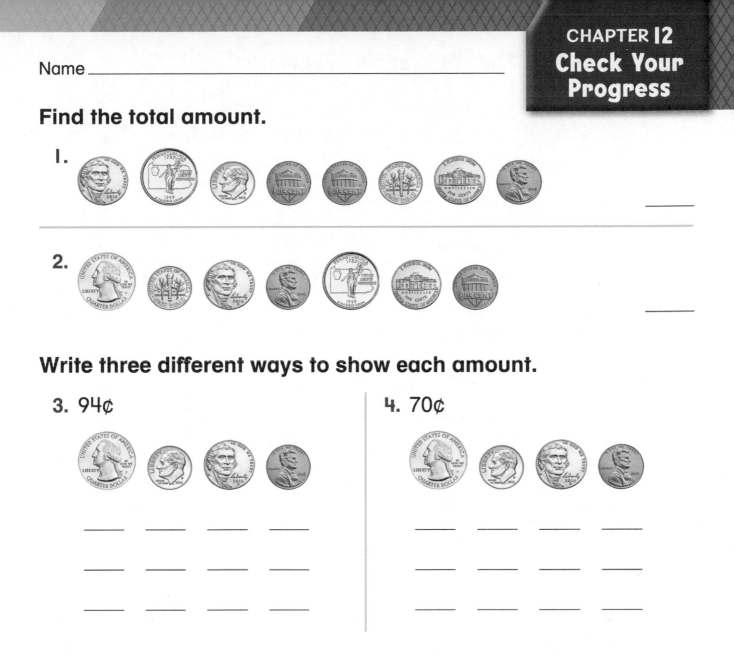
_____

2. _____

Write three different ways to show each amount.

3. 94¢

___ ___ ___ ___

___ ___ ___ ___

___ ___ ___ ___

4. 70¢

___ ___ ___ ___

___ ___ ___ ___

___ ___ ___ ___

Compare the total amounts of the two groups of coins. Circle the group with the greater amount.

5.

A pen costs 78¢. The coins show the amount paid.
Write the amount of change for each amount paid.

6.  _____

_____

7. 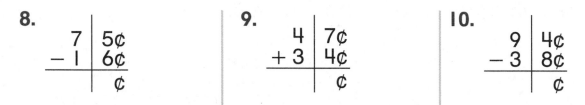 _____

Find the sum or difference. Regroup where needed.

8.
$$\begin{array}{r} 7\ |\ 5¢ \\ -\ 1\ |\ 6¢ \\ \hline \quad |\ \ ¢ \end{array}$$

9.
$$\begin{array}{r} 4\ |\ 7¢ \\ +\ 3\ |\ 4¢ \\ \hline \quad |\ \ ¢ \end{array}$$

10.
$$\begin{array}{r} 9\ |\ 4¢ \\ -\ 3\ |\ 8¢ \\ \hline \quad |\ \ ¢ \end{array}$$

Show $1 in three ways.

11.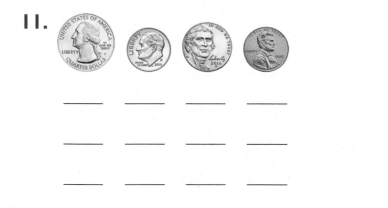

___ ___ ___ ___

___ ___ ___ ___

___ ___ ___ ___

Show two different ways to make the given amount.

12. $215

_____ $100 bills, _____ $10 bill, and _____ $5 bill

or

_____ $50 bills, _____ $10 bill, and _____ $5 bill

CHAPTER 12 Check Your Progress

Name _____

Hour and Half Hour

Travis practices his trumpet in the afternoon. What time does he start practicing? What time does he end?

Objective
- Tell and write time to the hour and half hour.

Math Words
minute hand
hour hand
minute
hour
half hour
half past

Start: End:

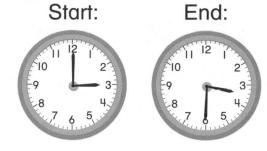

- First, find the time Travis starts practicing.

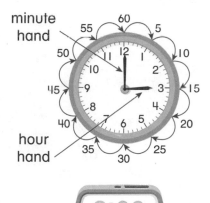

When the minute hand points to twelve, it is the beginning of an hour.

1 hour = 60 minutes

3:00 ↑ hour minutes

Read as: 3 o'clock

- Then, find the time Travis stops practicing.

Notice that the hour hand is halfway between 3 and 4.

When the minute hand points to six, it is halfway through an hour.

1 half hour = 30 minutes

3:30

Read as: three thirty or
half past 3 or
30 minutes after 3

Travis starts practicing at 3:00 and ends at 3:30.

Write the time in two ways.

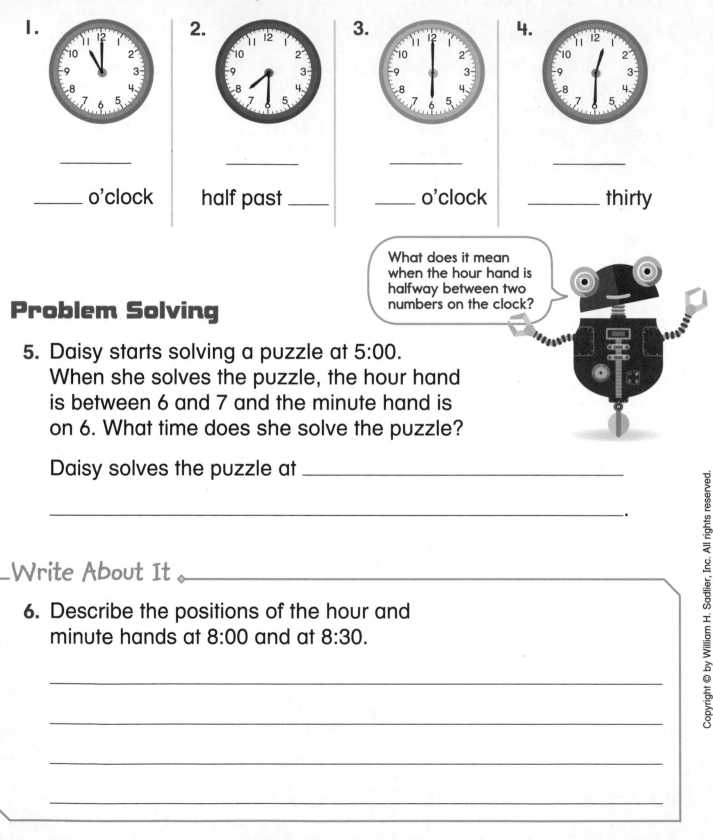

1.

_____ o'clock

2.

half past _____

3.

_____ o'clock

4.

_____ thirty

What does it mean when the hour hand is halfway between two numbers on the clock?

Problem Solving

5. Daisy starts solving a puzzle at 5:00. When she solves the puzzle, the hour hand is between 6 and 7 and the minute hand is on 6. What time does she solve the puzzle?

   Daisy solves the puzzle at _____

   _____.

Write About It

6. Describe the positions of the hour and minute hands at 8:00 and at 8:30.

   _____

   _____

   _____

   _____

Name _____

Hour and Half Hour

Find the start and end times shown by the clocks.

Start

minute
hand

hour
hand

3:00

↑ └─┘
hour minutes

Read as:
3 o'clock

End

3:30

Read as: three thirty
or
half past 3
or
30 minutes
after 3

▷ The start time is 3:00 and the end time is 3:30.

MORE PRACTICE

Write the time in two ways.

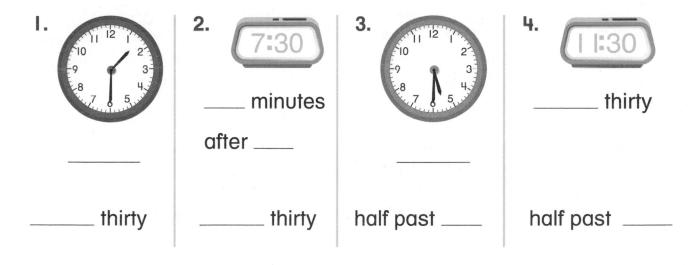

1.

_____

_____ thirty

2.

7:30

_____ minutes

after ____

_____ thirty

3.

_____

half past ____

4.

11:30

_____ thirty

half past ____

Match the clocks to the correct time.

1.

    A. 1 o'clock

2.

    B. 10 o'clock

3.

    C. half past 4

Problem Solving

4. Catherine sets her clock to 7:30. Where should Catherine point the hands of her clock?

   The hour hand should point halfway between ____ and ____.

   The minute hand should point to ____.

─Write About It

5. How can you tell if a time is on the hour or at the half hour by looking only at the hour hand?

   _____

   _____

   _____

Name _____

Five Minutes

Chelsea's art class starts at the time shown. At what time does her art class start?

Objective
• Tell and write time to the nearest five minutes.

Math Words
hour hand
minute hand
hour
minute

• To find the hour, look at the shorter hand. This is the hour hand.

The hour hand moves very slowly from 2 to 3. Say 2 as the hour until the hour hand points exactly to 3. Then the hour will be 3.

The hour is 2.

• To find the minutes, start at 12. Count by 5s until you reach the minute hand.

The minute hand points to 7. Count by 5s seven times: 5, 10, 15, 20, 25, 30, 35.

The minutes are 35.

The art class starts at 35 minutes after 2, or 2:35.

Digital clocks show you what the hours and minutes are.

Write the time in two ways.

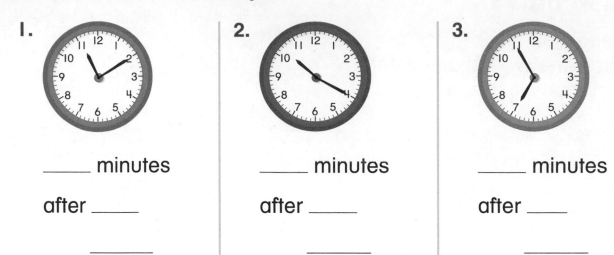

1.

_____ minutes

after _____

_____

2.

_____ minutes

after _____

_____

3.

_____ minutes

after _____

_____

Problem Solving

4. Lucy leaves to go to the library at 3:15.
When she gets to the library, the minute
hand has moved and points to 5.
The hour hand has hardly moved.
What time does Lucy get to the library?

Lucy gets to the library at _____.

Write About It

5. How is counting minutes on a clock like
counting tally marks?

_____

_____

_____

_____

_____

Name _____

Five Minutes

Find the time shown on the clock.

To find the hour, look at the shorter hand. It is between 2 and 3. Say 2 as the hour until the hour hand points exactly to 3.

The hour is 2.

To find the minutes, start at 12. Since the minute hand points to 7, count by 5s seven times:

5, 10, 15, 20, 25, 30, 35.

The minutes are 35.

The time is 35 minutes after 2. It is 2:35.

MORE PRACTICE

Write the time in two ways.

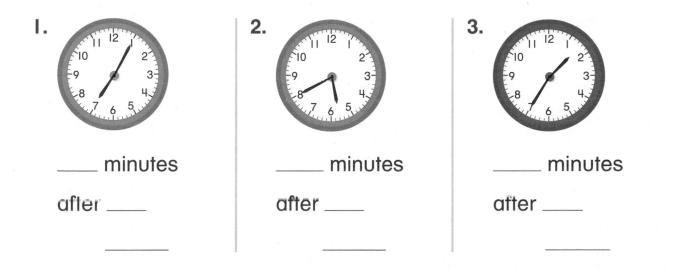

1.

_____ minutes

after _____

_____

2.

_____ minutes

after _____

_____

3.

_____ minutes

after _____

_____

Draw the minute hand to show the time.

1.

2.

3.

Problem Solving

4. Kennedy sets her watch to show 11:45.
   Where does she set the hands of the
   watch to point?

   The hour hand points between ____ and ____.

   The minute hand points to ____.

Write About It

5. Kelly sees that the longer hand of the
   kitchen clock points to 1 and the shorter
   hand points to 7. She says the time is 1:35.
   Is Kelly correct? Explain.

   _____

   _____

   _____

   _____

LESSON 12-10

A.M. and P.M.

Practice for the school play starts at 3:45.

Is the time A.M. or P.M.?

Think about what part of the day practice happens.

Objective
- Tell and write time to the nearest five minutes using A.M. and P.M.

Math Words

A.M.

P.M.

- Use the letters A.M. to show a time after midnight and before noon.

- Use the letters P.M. to show a time after noon and before midnight.

Practice for the play is in the afternoon.
Use P.M. to show the time.

> Practice for the school play starts at 3:45 P.M.
> Many digital clocks show A.M. or P.M. after the time.

PRACTICE

Write the time. Circle A.M. or P.M.

1.

You eat breakfast at

_____   A.M.   P.M.

2.

You eat supper at

_____   A.M.   P.M.

Write the time for each activity. Use A.M. or P.M.

3.

wake up

_____

4.

do homework

_____

5.

go to bed

_____

Problem Solving

6. Jillian has volleyball practice on Saturday. Practice starts at half past 11 and goes until 15 minutes after 12. What time does practice start and end?
Use A.M. or P.M.

Practice starts at _____ and

ends at _____.

Write About It

7. If the time is 12:05 A.M., is it just after midnight or just after noon? Explain how you know.

_____

_____

_____

_____

Name _____

A.M. **and** P.M.

The time shown is in the afternoon.
Give the time using A.M. or P.M.

Use the letters A.M. to show a time after midnight and before noon.

Use the letters P.M. to show a time after noon and before midnight.

Morning times are A.M.
Afternoon and evening times are P.M.

▷ The time is in the afternoon so it is 3:45 P.M.

MORE PRACTICE

Write the time for each activity. Use A.M. **or** P.M.

1.

start school

_____

2.

get on school bus

_____

3.

clean your room

_____

4.

eat dessert

_____

5.

have a snack

_____

6.

have music class

_____

**Draw the hands on the clock to show each time.
Then write the time using A.M. or P.M.**

1. get out of bed

`6:25`

_____

2. play outside

`4:30`

_____

3. get dressed
for school

`7:05`

_____

Problem Solving

4. Rob gets home from school at 40 minutes after 3.
   What time does he get home? Use A.M. or P.M.

   Rob gets home at _____.

Write About It

5. Derek says he will meet Ivan at the park at 7:30.
   The next day, both boys go to the same place
   at the park at 7:30, but they do not meet.
   What could have happened?

   _____

   _____

   _____

Name_____

Problem Solving   Read ⟩ Plan ⟩ Solve ⟩ Check
Work Backward

Objective
- Work backward for a given problem-solving situation.

Math Word
work backward

Miguel goes to the library for 1 hour after school. Then he bikes home in 15 minutes. He spends 45 minutes working on homework before he has dinner at 5:30 P.M. What time did Miguel get to the library?

You can work backward to solve the problem.

- First, find the time Miguel started his homework. Count back 45 minutes from 5:30 P.M.

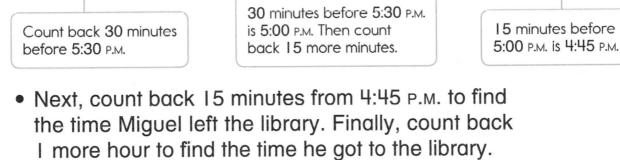

Count back 30 minutes before 5:30 P.M.

30 minutes before 5:30 P.M. is 5:00 P.M. Then count back 15 more minutes.

15 minutes before 5:00 P.M. is 4:45 P.M.

- Next, count back 15 minutes from 4:45 P.M. to find the time Miguel left the library. Finally, count back 1 more hour to find the time he got to the library.

15 minutes before 4:45 P.M. is 4:30 P.M.

1 hour before 4:30 P.M. is 3:30 P.M.

Miguel got to the library at 3:30 P.M.

Read and solve each problem. You can work backward to help solve some of the problems.

1. Nathan had some money to start. Then he gets $35 for his birthday. He spends $42 on a trip to a museum. Now, he has $17 left. How much money did Nathan start with?

   Nathan had _____ to start.

2. Giselle's bike lock uses a three-digit number. The ones digit is 3 less than the hundreds digit. The hundreds digit is 7. The tens digit is an odd number. What are the possible bike lock numbers?

   The number could be _____.

3. Mia is working on a school project. It takes her one and one half hours to write a report. Then she spends 45 minutes making a graph for the report. If Mia finishes at 2:15 P.M., what time did she start?

   Mia started her project at _____

Write About It

4. Explain how you found the time Mia started her project.

   _____

   _____

   _____

   _____

Problem Solving
Work Backward

Miguel goes to the library for 1 hour after school. Then he bikes home in 15 minutes. He spends 45 minutes on homework before he has dinner at 5:30 P.M. What time did Miguel get to the library?

- First, work backward to find the time Miguel started his homework. Count back 45 minutes from 5:30 P.M.

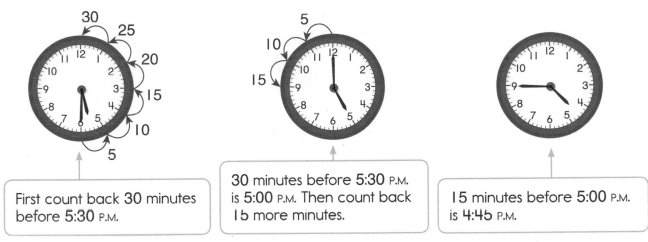

First count back 30 minutes before 5:30 P.M.

30 minutes before 5:30 P.M. is 5:00 P.M. Then count back 15 more minutes.

15 minutes before 5:00 P.M. is 4:45 P.M.

- Next, count back 15 minutes from 4:45 P.M. to find the time Miguel left the library. Finally, count back 1 more hour to find the time he got to the library.

15 minutes before 4:45 P.M. is 4:30 P.M.

1 hour before 4:30 P.M. is 3:30 P.M.

Miguel got to the library at 3:30 P.M.

Read and solve each problem. You can work backward to help solve some of the problems.

1. After he wakes up, Eduardo spends 30 minutes getting ready for school in the morning. Then, he spends 25 minutes eating breakfast and 15 minutes walking to school. If he gets to school at 8:00 A.M., what time did Eduardo wake up?

   Eduardo woke up at _____

2. A pet store orders 500 bags of dog treats. At the end of the first week, there are 386 bags left. The next week, they sell 115 bags. How many bags are left now? How many bags of dog treats were sold in all?

   The pet store has _____ bags left.

   The pet store sold _____ bags of dog treats.

3. Omar has some coins to start. He finds 1 quarter and 3 pennies. Then, he spends 45¢ on a juice box. Now Omar has 18¢. How much money did he have to start?

   Omar had _____ to start.

4. An art studio opens with a one-hour pottery class. Then, there is a 45-minute drawing class that ends at 11:15 A.M. What time does the studio open?

   The studio opens at _____

HOMEWORK

Read and solve each problem. You can work backward to help solve some of the problems.

1. Mateo buys a skateboard for $57, a helmet for $23, and some knee and elbow pads for $32. If he gets $88 in change, how much did Mateo give the cashier?

   Mateo gave _____ to the cashier.

2. Sophie leaves school and walks home in 5 minutes. She spends 15 minutes having a snack. Then, Sophie spends 1 hour playing outside. She finishes at 5:00 P.M. What time did Sophie leave school?

   Sophie left school at _____

3. Chase gets 345 points in the first round of a video game. He loses 120 points in the next round. In the third round, Chase gets 217 points. What is his final score?

   Chase's final score is _____ points.

4. Crystal, Bailey, Kiara, and Lisa have a running race. Bailey does not finish first, but she does not finish last. Crystal finishes before Lisa, but after Bailey. In what order do the girls finish the race?

   The order is _____.

Read and solve each problem. You can work backward to help solve some of the problems.

5. Vanessa has some money to start. She earns $25 raking her neighbor's leaves and $15 running errands. Then, she spends $12 at a store. Now Vanessa has $52 left. How much money did she have to start?

   Vanessa had _____ to start.

6. Kyle draws three numbers from a deck of cards. He draws a 6, an 8, and a 5. What is the difference of the greatest and least three-digit numbers that Kyle can make with the cards?

   The difference is _____.

7. On a rainy day, Lauren spends 1 hour and 15 minutes playing board games with her brother and 2 hours reading. If Lauren finishes reading at 2:45 P.M., what time did she start playing board games with her brother?

   Lauren started playing board games at _____.

Write About It

8. Explain how you found the time Lauren started playing board games with her brother.

   _____

   _____

Name _____

Find the total amount.

1.

_____

Circle Yes or No to tell if the groups of coins show equal amounts. If they do not, circle the group with the greater amount.

2.

Yes

No

A peach costs 62¢. The coins show the amount paid. Write the amount of change given.

3.

_____

Find the sum or difference. Regroup where needed.

4. 90¢ − 32¢ = _____   5. 33¢ + 59¢ = _____

Find the total amount.

6.

_____

Write the time shown.

7. _____

8. _____

9. _____

10. _____

Draw the hands on the clock to show each time. Then write the time using A.M. or P.M.

11. watch sunset

6:50

_____

12. have snack

10:10

_____

13. get to school

8:30

_____

Work backward to solve.

14. Maddie wakes up in the morning and spends 30 minutes reading in bed. Then she spends 15 minutes eating breakfast and 25 minutes getting ready for school. Maddie is ready to leave for school at 7:25 A.M. What time did she wake up?

Maddie woke up at _____

Name _____

The U.S. Mint has other coin programs besides the quarter programs. Presidential $1 Coins show presidents of the United States.

1. From 2007 to 2015, the U.S. Mint minted and issued four Presidential $1 Coins each year. What is the total value of four $1 coins?

   $____

2. Ella has a $1 coin. She wants to trade with Liz for state quarters. How many quarters should Liz give Ella for the girls to have equal amounts?

   ____ quarters

3. Gage buys a yo-yo for 93¢. He gives the store a $1 coin. How much change should Gage receive?

   Gage should receive ____¢ change.

4. Research another coin program at the U.S. Mint, such as Native American Dollar Coins or American Buffalo Coins.

   • Write down 3 facts about the coin program. Include information about the coins' designs.

   • Ask and answer 3 questions about the values of the coins you research.

   • Share your facts and questions with a partner.

   • Answer your partner's questions and discuss how you found your answers.

Name _____

Determine the best answer for each problem.

1. Use mental math to add.

$530 + 300 =$ _____

2. Use mental math to subtract.

$809 - 40 =$ _____

3. What is the value of the digit 7 in 749?

_____

4. What is the value of the digit 3 in 231?

_____

5. Subtract.

$$\begin{array}{r} 624 \\ -318 \\ \hline \end{array}$$

6. Add.

$$\begin{array}{r} 483 \\ +329 \\ \hline \end{array}$$

7. Add.

$$\begin{array}{r} 284 \\ +329 \\ \hline \end{array}$$

8. Subtract.

$$\begin{array}{r} 405 \\ -182 \\ \hline \end{array}$$

9. Which is the expanded form of 503?

A. $5 + 0 + 3$

B. $50 + 3$

C. $500 + 3$

D. $500 + 30$

10. Which two answers have a sum greater than 100?

A. $18 + 84$

B. $23 + 77$

C. $43 + 58$

D. $65 + 34$

E. $74 + 23$

Geometry

CENTRAL PARK

WEST CENTER EAST

When you go somewhere new like a city, park, or shopping mall, you can use a map to help find your way around. You can find those maps on signs, on paper, and even on mobile devices!

Types of Maps

◆ Reference maps, like road maps, show where places are located and how to get there from where you are.

◆ Topographic maps are special kinds of maps. They show the shape, or topography, of the land.

Reading Maps

◆ Scientists who make maps are called cartographers. They use symbols to describe an area.

◆ Find out how cartographers use symbols to show mountains, lakes, and forests.

Dear Family,

In this chapter, we will be learning about two-dimensional and three-dimensional shapes.

Here are some key **Math Words** for this chapter:

polygon	**pentagon**
side	**hexagon**
angle	**face**
triangle	**edge**
quadrilateral	**vertex**

You can use the glossary to find the definition of each word and help your child make flash cards to study each day.

During this chapter we will also be making STEAM (Science, Technology, Engineering, the Arts, and Mathematics) connections about shapes and symbols on topographic maps. Read the opening to the chapter together.

Keep Your Skills Sharp

Here is a **Keep Your Skills Sharp** activity to do at home to prepare for this chapter.

Help your child find two- and three-dimensional shapes. When looking at solid figures, explore the shapes that make up each face. For example, if you are playing a board game, point out the 6 squares that make up the faces of a number cube.

Identify Two-Dimensional Shapes

Objective
- Identify triangles, quadrilaterals, pentagons, and hexagons.

Math Words
polygon
two-dimensional
side
angle
triangle
quadrilateral
pentagon
hexagon

While playing baseball, Blake looks at home plate. What shape is home plate?

Home plate is a polygon.

Polygons are flat, or two-dimensional, closed figures with straight sides.

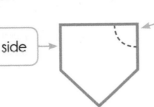

side

An angle is the space between two sides that meet.

Types of Polygons

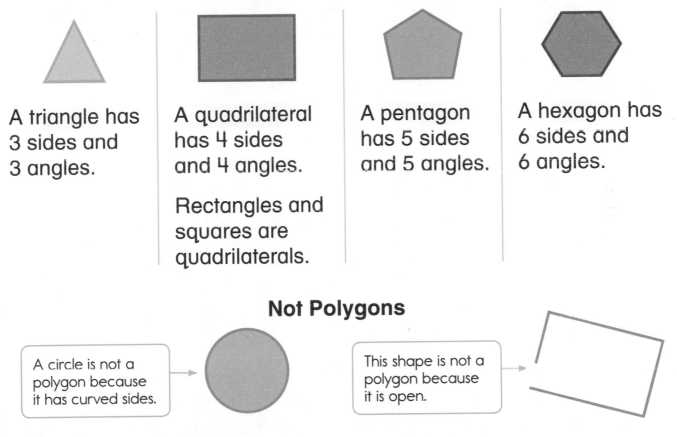

A triangle has 3 sides and 3 angles.

A quadrilateral has 4 sides and 4 angles.

Rectangles and squares are quadrilaterals.

A pentagon has 5 sides and 5 angles.

A hexagon has 6 sides and 6 angles.

Not Polygons

A circle is not a polygon because it has curved sides.

This shape is not a polygon because it is open.

Home plate has 5 sides and 5 angles, so it is a pentagon.

Circle *polygon* or *not a polygon* to describe the shape. If it is a polygon, write its name.

1.

polygon   not a polygon

_____

2.

polygon   not a polygon

_____

Match the polygon with its name.

3.   4.   5.

A. triangle   **B.** quadrilateral   **C.** pentagon

Problem Solving

6. Abby draws a rectangle. Lily draws a shape with 2 more sides and angles than Abby's rectangle. What polygon does Lily draw?

Lily draws a _____.

Write About It

7. Aaron draws a quadrilateral with four square corners and four equal sides. He says that the shape is a rectangle. Is Aaron correct? Explain.

_____

_____

Name _____

Identify Two-Dimensional Shapes

Polygons are flat, or two-dimensional, closed figures with straight sides.

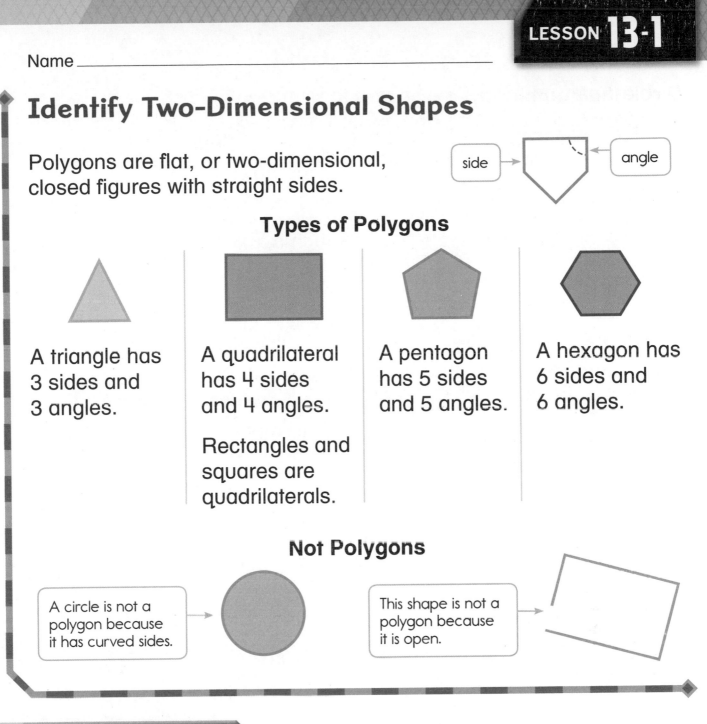

Types of Polygons

A triangle has 3 sides and 3 angles.

A quadrilateral has 4 sides and 4 angles.

Rectangles and squares are quadrilaterals.

A pentagon has 5 sides and 5 angles.

A hexagon has 6 sides and 6 angles.

Not Polygons

A circle is not a polygon because it has curved sides.

This shape is not a polygon because it is open.

MORE PRACTICE

If the shape is a polygon, write its name.
If it is not a polygon, write *not a polygon.*

1.

_____

2.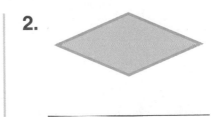

_____

Write the name of the polygon.

1. This polygon has 2 fewer sides than a pentagon.

   _____

2. This polygon has 3 more angles than a triangle.

   _____

Complete the table.

3.

Name of Polygon	Number of Sides	Number of Angles
triangle		
	4	
		5
hexagon		

Problem Solving

4. Jeff sees this sign near his school. What shape is the sign?

   The sign is a _____.

Write About It

5. How do you decide whether or not a shape is a polygon?

   _____

   _____

   _____

Draw Two-Dimensional Shapes

LESSON **13-2**

Objective
■ Draw triangles, quadrilaterals, pentagons, and hexagons.

Math Words
polygon
angle
triangle
quadrilateral
pentagon
hexagon

Courtney draws one side of a polygon on dot paper. What are some ways Courtney can complete her drawing to make a hexagon?

Every hexagon has 6 sides.
So Courtney needs to draw 5 more sides.

➡ There are many different hexagons Courtney could draw. Here are some of them.

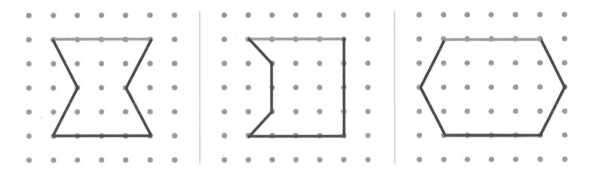

PRACTICE

Use the dot paper to complete the polygon.

1. pentagon

2. rectangle

Name the shape. Then draw an example of the shape on dot paper.

3. Luis draws a polygon with 6 sides. What shape does he draw?

_____

4. The sign near Melissa's house is a polygon with 5 angles. What shape is the sign?

_____

Problem Solving

5. Micah draws two polygons. They have a total of 7 sides. What polygons does Micah draw?

   Micah draws a _____ and a _____.

Write About It

6. If you and a friend each draw a hexagon on dot paper, how will the drawings be the same? How might they be different?

   _____

   _____

   _____

   _____

Name _____

Draw Two-Dimensional Shapes

A hexagon has 6 sides.

Draw a hexagon with the given side.

There are many different hexagons you could draw.

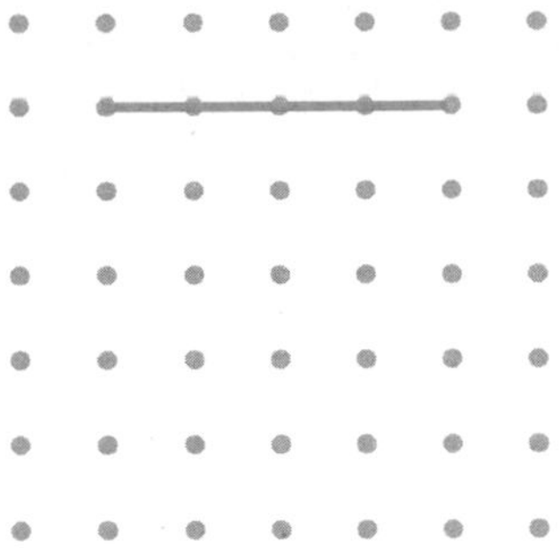

Use the dots to help you.

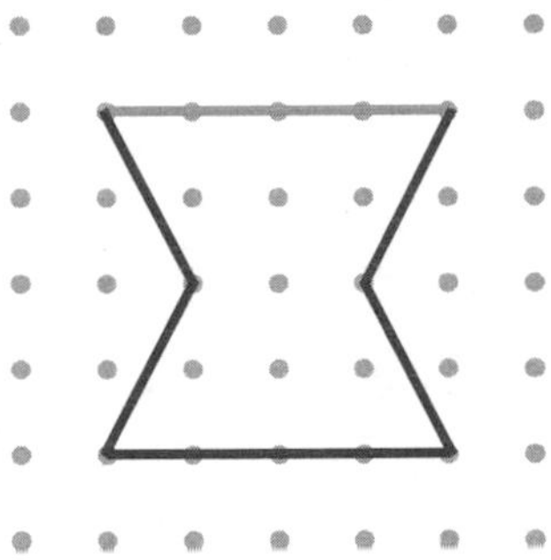

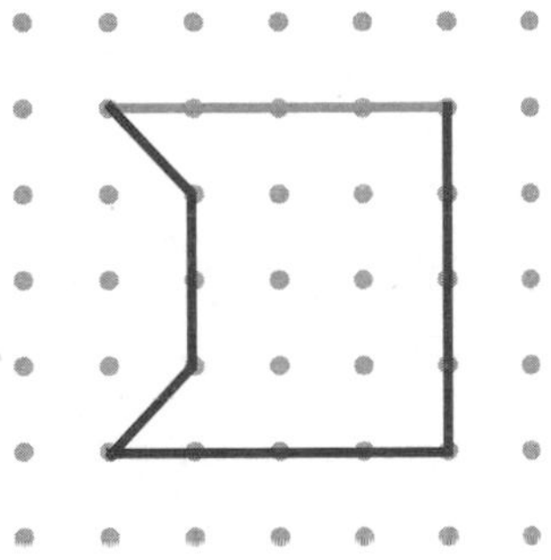

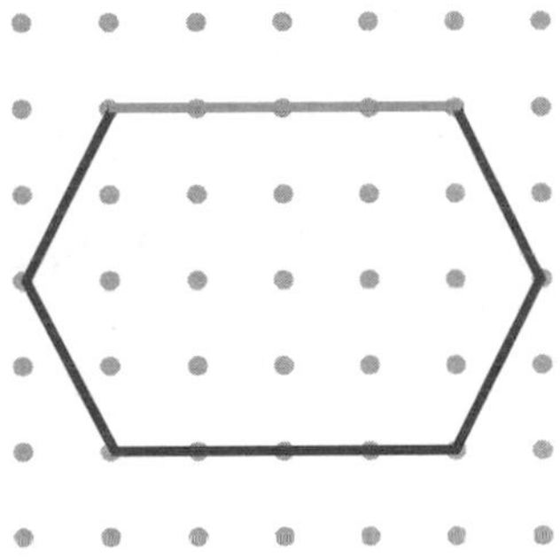

Each of the hexagons has 6 sides.

MORE PRACTICE

Use the dot paper to complete the polygon.

1. triangle

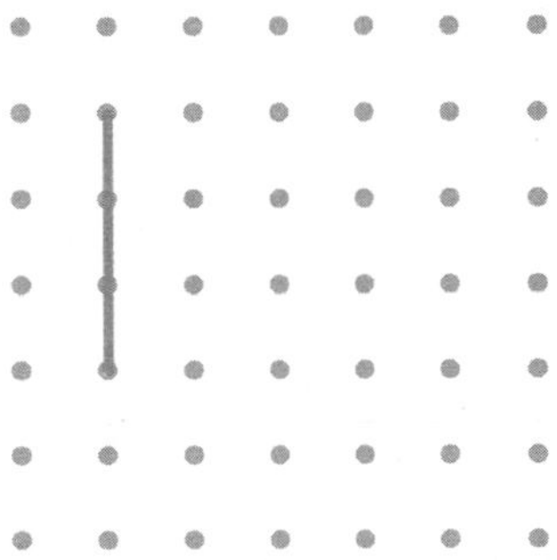

2. hexagon

3. square

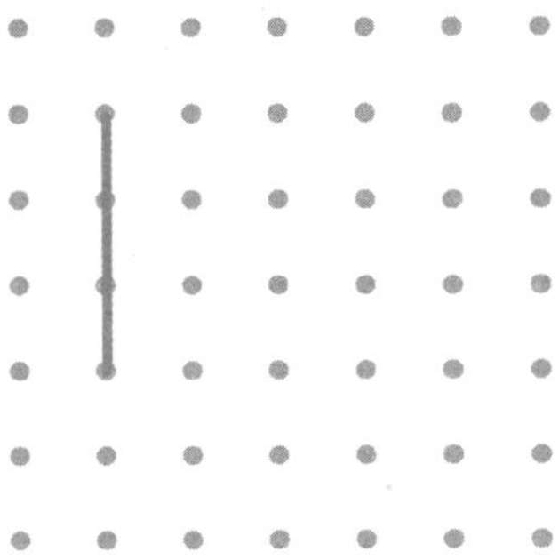

Use the dot paper to draw three different pentagons.

1.

2.

3.

Problem Solving

4. Giselle has two buttons in the shapes of polygons. One button has 6 sides, and the other has 3 fewer sides. Draw an example of each button.

Write About It

5. Tamara draws two polygons that have a total of 9 angles. What polygons could Tamara have drawn? Explain.

_____

_____

_____

Name _____

**If the shape is a polygon, write its name.
If it is not a polygon, write *not a polygon*.**

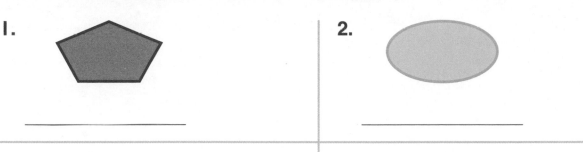

1. _____

2. _____

3. a closed figure with 3 straight sides and 1 curved side

_____

4. a closed figure with 4 angles and 4 straight sides

_____

Solve.

5. Angelica draws two polygons. The first polygon has 6 angles. The second polygon has 2 fewer angles. What polygons might she have drawn?

   Angelica draws a _____ and a _____.

   What is the total number of sides in the two polygons she draws?

   Angelica draws _____ sides in the two polygons.

6. Xavier makes a polygon using toothpicks. The shape has 2 more sides than a triangle. What shape does he make?

   Xavier makes a _____.

   Then, Xavier changes the shape so it has one fewer side. What shape might he have now?

   Xavier now has a _____.

Use the dot paper to draw the polygon.

7. hexagon	8. polygon with 4 angles	9. polygon with 5 sides
. . . . . .	. . . . . .	. . . . . .
. . . . . .	. . . . . .	. . . . . .
. . . . . .	. . . . . .	. . . . . .
. . . . . .	. . . . . .	. . . . . .
. . . . . .	. . . . . .	. . . . . .
. . . . . .	. . . . . .	. . . . . .
. . . . . .	. . . . . .	. . . . . .

Circle the name of the polygon.

10. a polygon with 4 sides and 4 angles

    A. triangle

    B. pentagon

    C. quadrilateral

11. a polygon with 1 more side than a pentagon

    A. quadrilateral

    B. hexagon

    C. triangle

12. a polygon with 2 more angles than a triangle

    A. pentagon

    B. quadrilateral

    C. hexagon

Name _____

Identify Three-Dimensional Shapes

Objective
- Identify cones, cubes, cylinders, pyramids, rectangular prisms, and spheres.

Mia heats up a can of soup for lunch. What shape is the soup can?

The soup can is a three-dimensional shape, or solid figure.

Three-dimensional figures that roll smoothly have a curved surface.

 ← flat surface

← curved surface

Three-dimensional figures that cannot roll have all flat surfaces.

Some three-dimensional figures have both flat and curved surfaces.

A cylinder has a top and bottom that are flat surfaces, and a side that is a curved surface.

Math Words

three-
  dimensional
cube
pyramid
rectangular
  prism
cone
sphere
cylinder

    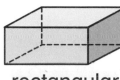

cube   pyramid   rectangular   cone   sphere   cylinder
              prism

➡ The soup can is a cylinder.

PRACTICE

Write the name of the three-dimensional figure the object is shaped like.

1.

_____

2.

_____

Match the three-dimensional figure with its name.

3. 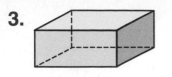   **A.** cube

4.   **B.** rectangular prism

5.   **C.** cone

6.   **D.** pyramid

Problem Solving

7. Andres makes a three-dimensional figure out of clay. His figure has I flat surface and I curved surface. What figure does Andres make?

   Andres makes a _____.

Write About It

8. Nate says that he has a wooden block with all flat surfaces. Is that enough information to know what three-dimensional figure the block is shaped like? Why or why not?

   _____

   _____

   _____

Name _____

Identify Three-Dimensional Shapes

A three-dimensional figure can have flat surfaces, curved surfaces, or both.

Three-dimensional figures that roll smoothly have a curved surface.

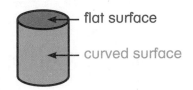
flat surface
curved surface

Three-dimensional figures that cannot roll have all flat surfaces.

There are different types of three-dimensional figures.

  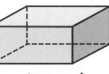

| cube | pyramid | rectangular prism | cone | sphere | cylinder |

MORE PRACTICE

Write the name of the three-dimensional figure the object is shaped like.

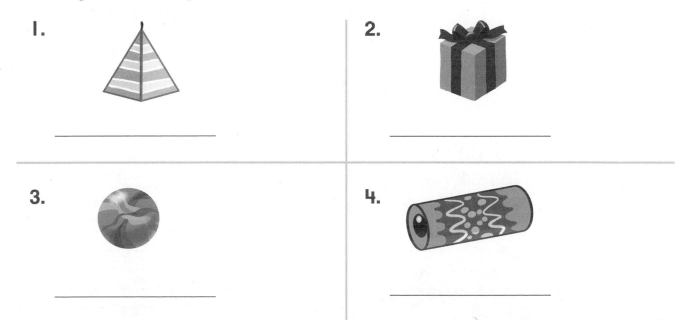

1.

_____

2.

_____

3.

_____

4.

_____

Write the letter or letters to tell the correct answers.

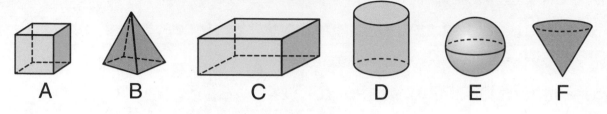

A   B   C   D   E   F

1. Which shape has no flat surfaces? _____

2. Which shapes have all flat surfaces? _____

3. Which shape has 1 flat surface and

   1 curved surface? _____

4. Which shape has all flat surfaces that are

   the same shape? _____

Problem Solving

5. Ashe has a cylinder and a cone. What is the total
   number of flat surfaces on the two figures?

   There are ____ flat surfaces in all.

Write About It

6. Daniela is making a bracelet. She says that the
   purple bead has a curved surface. Is that enough
   information to know what three-dimensional figure
   the purple bead is shaped like? Why or why not?

   _____

   _____

Name _____

Faces, Edges, and Vertices

Objectives
- Identify the faces, edges, and vertices of three-dimensional figures.
- Draw a cube.

Math Words
face
edge
vertex (plural vertices)
corner

Randy wants to paint each face of a cube a different color. How many colors will Randy need? How can Randy draw a cube?

Three-dimensional figures with all flat surfaces have faces, edges, and vertices.

A face is a flat surface with straight lines.

An edge is where two faces meet.

A vertex is a point where three or more edges meet. A vertex is also called a corner.

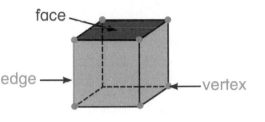

A cube has 6 faces, 12 edges, and 8 vertices.

You can use dot paper to draw a cube.
Each face of a cube is shaped like a square.

Start by drawing a square.	Draw equal slanted lines from the square's vertices.	Connect the ends of the lines.

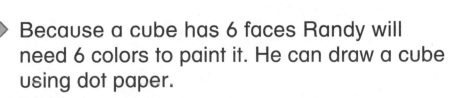

Because a cube has 6 faces Randy will need 6 colors to paint it. He can draw a cube using dot paper.

Complete the table. Use solid objects to help you.

	Figure	Faces	Edges	Vertices
1.		0	0	
2.			12	
3.		5		
4.				0

Remember that faces have straight, not curved, edges.

Name the figure and draw it on dot paper.

5. a three-dimensional figure with 6 equal faces

The figure is a _____.

Problem Solving

6. Vic has a three-dimensional figure with 4 fewer edges than a cube. What is Vic's figure?

Vic has a _____.

⸻ Write About It ⸻

7. Explain why cones and cylinders have 0 vertices.

_____

_____

Name_____

Faces, Edges, and Vertices

Three-dimensional figures with all flat surfaces have faces, edges, and vertices.

A face is a flat surface with straight edges.

An edge is where two faces meet.

A vertex is where three edges meet.

A cube has 6 faces, 8 vertices, and 12 edges.

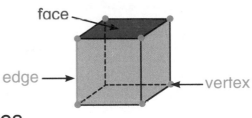

face
edge
vertex

You can use dot paper to draw a cube.

| Start by drawing a square. | Draw equal slanted lines from the square's vertices. | Connect the ends of the lines. |

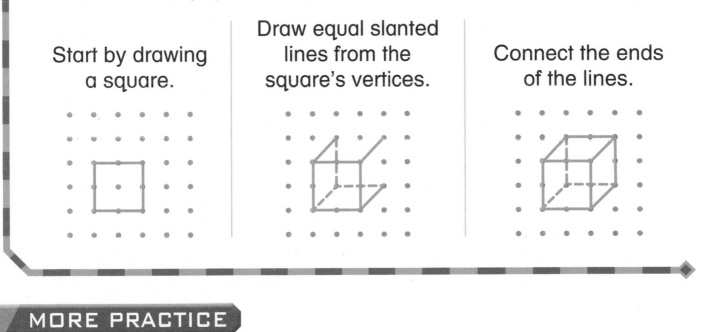

MORE PRACTICE

Use the dot paper to complete the rectangular prism.

1.

Match the description with the figure.

1. a figure with 2 square faces and 4 rectangular faces

   A.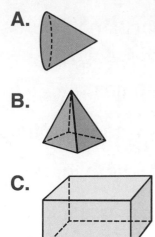

2. a figure with 0 faces

   B.

3. a figure with 5 vertices

   C.

Problem Solving

4. Sergio has a three-dimensional figure. It has 3 more vertices than a pyramid. What figure could Sergio have?

   Sergio could have a _____.

5. Jordyn has two different three-dimensional figures. They have a total of 11 faces. What figures could Jordyn have?

   Jordyn could have a _____ and a _____.

Write About It

6. Explain how you found the figures Jordyn could have.

   _____

   _____

   _____

Name_____

Problem Solving 〉Read〉Plan〉Solve〉Check〉
Use Logical Reasoning

Kelly says that if she folds the diagram on the dashed lines, it will make a cone. Tameka says it will make a pyramid. Who is correct?

To find who is correct, use logical reasoning.

Think about the shapes in the diagram. Each shape is one face of the three-dimensional figure.

This shape is a square. It could be the bottom face of the figure. →

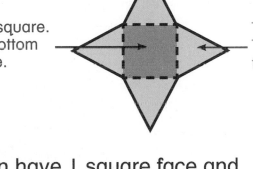

← This shape is a triangle. The 4 triangles could be the 4 sides of the figure.

A pyramid can have 1 square face and 4 faces that are triangles.

You can fold on the dashed lines so each of the triangular faces points up toward the middle, forming a pyramid. The point where the faces meet is a vertex.

▷ The figure is a pyramid, so Tameka is correct.

Use logical reasoning to solve the problem.

1. Lucy folds this diagram to make a three-dimensional figure. What figure does Lucy make?

   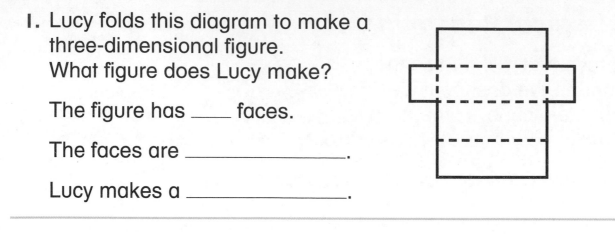

   The figure has ____ faces.

   The faces are _____.

   Lucy makes a _____.

2. Tracy folds a diagram to make a three-dimensional figure. Two of the shapes in the diagram are circles. What three-dimensional figure does Tracy make?

   Tracy makes a _____.

3. Bryan gets a present in a box shaped like a cube. Circle the diagram that could be folded to make a cube.

   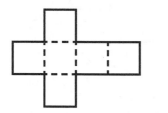   

─Write About It ◇──────────────────

4. Explain how you chose which diagram could be folded to make a cube.

   _____

   _____

   _____

Problem Solving
Use Logical Reasoning

Kelly folds the diagram on the dashed lines.
What three-dimensional figure does she make?

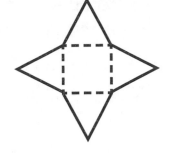

Use logical reasoning.
Think about the shapes in the diagram.

This shape is a square.
It could be the bottom
face of the figure. — 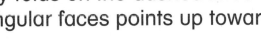 This shape is a triangle.
The 4 triangles could be
the 4 sides of the figure.

A pyramid can have 1 square face and
4 triangular faces.

Kelly folds on the dashed lines so each of the
triangular faces points up toward the middle.

⟹ Kelly makes a pyramid.

MORE PRACTICE

Use logical reasoning to solve the problem.

1. Ben's favorite cereal comes in a box shaped
   like a rectangular prism. What shapes make
   up the faces of the cereal box?

   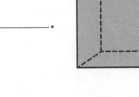

   The cereal box is made up of _____.

   How many? _____

Use logical reasoning to solve the problems.

2. Claire cuts pieces of cardboard to make a three-dimensional figure. She cuts these pieces.

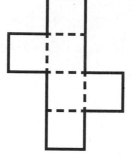

Then Claire draws a diagram to plan how she will tape the pieces together. What figure does Claire make?

Claire makes a _____.

3. Layla's soccer jersey has a two-digit number. Both digits are even. The digit in the tens place is 4 more than the digit in the ones place. List all possible numbers for Layla's soccer jersey.

_____

4. Caleb's garden has 3 rows of 3 tomato plants and 2 rows of 6 pepper plants. Luke's garden has 5 rows of 5 cucumber plants. Whose garden has more plants? How many more?

_____'s garden has ____ more plants.

5. Otis and Nick are each folding a diagram of a three-dimensional figure. Otis folds a pyramid. Nick's figure has 1 more face and 3 more vertices than Otis's figure. What figure is Nick folding?

Nick is folding a _____.

Name_____

HOMEWORK

Use logical reasoning to solve the problems.

1. Piper cuts enough squares and triangles
   from construction paper to make 3 pyramids.
   How many of each shape does she cut?

   Piper cuts ____ squares and ____ triangles.

2. Wes has 4 more yellow balloons than
   red balloons. He has 3 fewer green balloons
   than red balloons. If Wes has 2 green balloons,
   how many balloons does he have in all?

   Wes has ____ balloons in all.

3. Serena has two different three-dimensional
   figures. The figures have a total of 20 edges.
   One of Serena's figures is a cube. What is
   the other figure?

   The other figure is a _____.

4. Nate folds this diagram to make
   a three-dimensional figure.
   What figure does Nate make?
   Explain how you know.

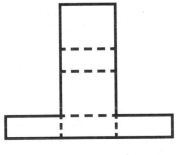

_____

_____

_____

Use logical reasoning to solve each problem.

5. A cafeteria serves 315 turkey sandwiches.
   It serves 87 fewer veggie sandwiches
   than turkey sandwiches. How many sandwiches
   does the cafeteria serve in all?

   _____ sandwiches

6. The sum of two numbers is 763. One of the
   numbers is 245. What is the difference of the
   two numbers?

   The difference is _____.

7. Hunter collects 394 cans for a food drive.
   Of the cans, 215 are beans and the rest are soup.
   How many more cans of beans than cans of soup
   does Hunter collect?

   Hunter collects _____ more cans of beans
   than cans of soup.

Write About It

8. Josh cuts 4 rectangles from cardboard. He plans
   to tape them together to make a rectangular prism.
   Will Josh be able to make this figure? Explain.

   _____

   _____

   _____

Name _____

**If the shape is a polygon, write its name.
If it is not a polygon, write *not a polygon*.**

1. _____

2. _____

Draw three different quadrilaterals.

3.

4.

5.

Solve.

6. Lena draws two polygons. The first polygon has 5 sides. The second polygon has 2 fewer sides than the first. What polygons does Lena draw?

   Lena draws a _____ and a _____.

7. Felix buys a toy that is in a box shaped like a pyramid. What shapes make up the faces of the box?

   The box is made up of ____ square

   and ____ _____.

Write the letter or letters that tell the correct answers.

A   B   C   D   E   F

8. Which figures have no faces and no vertices?

_____

9. Which figure is a pyramid? _____

10. Which figures have 6 faces? _____

11. Which figure has no flat surfaces? _____

12. Which figure has faces that are all the same?

_____

13. Which figure has 5 vertices? _____

Draw the three-dimensional figure.

14. a cube

15. a rectangular prism

Name _____

Jamal is drawing a topographic map of his town.

1. Jamal uses this symbol to show the town lake. Is the symbol in the shape of a polygon? Why or why not?

_____

_____

_____

2. Jamal colors in a section of his map to show the town forest. He wants to add a symbol to show that it is a forest and not grass. What polygon symbol could he use to show a forest? Explain your choice.

_____

_____

How many sides and angles does your choice of polygon have?

The polygon has ____ sides and ____ angles.

3. Find a topographic map of your town, city, or state.

• Look for the polygon symbols on the map. Use the legend, or key, to find what the symbols mean.

• Draw a topographic-style map of your neighborhood. Use polygon symbols to show the locations of different features. Be sure to include a legend so that others can read your map.

• Share your map with your class.

Determine the best answer for each problem.

1. Compare the sums.

   $18 + 27 \;\big(\; ? \;\big)\; 32 + 9$

   A. $<$
   B. $>$
   C. $=$

2. Compare the differences.

   $50 - 16 \;\big(\; ? \;\big)\; 61 - 27$

   A. $<$
   B. $>$
   C. $=$

3. Which is the expanded form of 830?

   A. $80 + 0 + 3$
   B. $800 + 0 + 3$
   C. $80 + 30 + 0$
   D. $800 + 30 + 0$

4. Which has a sum greater than 150?

   A. 7 tens + 9 tens
   B. 7 tens + 9 ones
   C. 7 ones + 9 tens
   D. 7 ones + 9 ones

5. Add.

   $56 + 25 + 4 = $ _____

6. Subtract.

   $91 - 45 = $ _____

7. Which have a sum of 100? Choose all that apply.

   A. $32 + 78$
   B. $45 + 45$
   C. $53 + 47$
   D. $61 + 39$

8. Which choices have a difference less than 30?

   A. $84 - 57$
   B. $77 - 45$
   C. $68 - 39$
   D. $61 - 31$

9. Find the unknown value.

   $309 + $ _____ $= 864$

10. Find the unknown value.

    $183 - $ _____ $= 116$

Equal Shares

Farmers organize their crops in rows. This makes it easier to care for all the plants. The plants can get their share of the space, soil, sunlight, and water they need to grow.

Water on the Farm

♦ Water for crops comes from many sources, like rainwater, rivers, and lakes.

♦ When there is not enough water from natural sources, farmers use machines or irrigation systems to water crops.

♦ Have you ever seen an irrigation system on a farm? How do you think farmers make sure their crops get an equal share of water?

Dear Family,

In this chapter, we will be learning about partitioning circles and rectangles into two, three, or four equal shares.

Here are some key **Math** Words for this chapter:

row	**whole**
column	**thirds**
array	**three thirds**
equal shares	**fourths**
half	**four fourths**
two halves	

You can use the glossary to find the definition of each word and help your child make flashcards to study each day we work on the lessons for this chapter.

During this chapter about equal shares, we will also be making STEAM (Science, Technology, Engineering, the Arts, and Mathematics) connections about water use and irrigation on farms. Read the opening to the chapter together.

Keep Your Skills Sharp

Here is a **Keep Your Skills Sharp** activity to do at home to prepare for this chapter.

Help your child partition items into equal shares. For example, when making lunch, ask your child to split a sandwich into 2 or 4 equal pieces. Or, look for shapes that are partitioned into 2, 3, or 4 parts. Discuss whether or not the parts are equal in size.

Name _____

Partition Rectangles into Rows and Columns

Objective
- Partition a rectangle into rows and columns of same-size squares. Count to find the total number of squares.

Math Words
row
column
array

Alice wants to cover two rectangles with same-size paper squares for an art project.

For which rectangle will Alice need more paper squares?

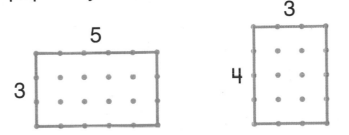

Draw lines to show same-size squares.
Then add the squares by row or by column.

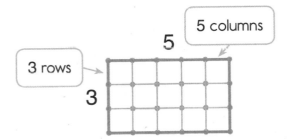

The blue rectangle is an array with 3 rows of 5 squares.

$5 + 5 + 5 = 15$

$3 + 3 + 3 + 3 + 3 = 15$

There are 15 squares in all.

The green rectangle is an array with 4 rows of 3 squares.

$3 + 3 + 3 + 3 = 12$

$4 + 4 + 4 = 12$

There are 12 squares in all.

> Alice needs more paper squares to cover the blue rectangle.

Draw lines to show same-size squares.
Then write the total number of squares.

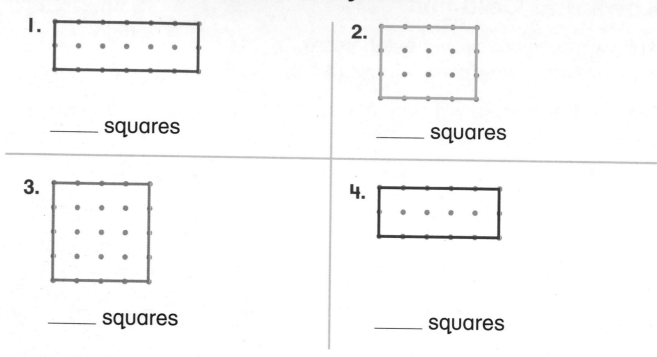

1.

_____ squares

2.

_____ squares

3.

_____ squares

4.

_____ squares

Problem Solving

5. Richard draws lines in a rectangle to show same-size squares. He makes 5 rows of 6 squares. What is the total number of squares in the rectangle? You can draw the squares on dot paper to help you.

_____ squares

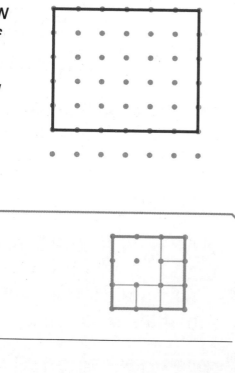

Write About It

6. Tess says that she drew lines in this rectangle to show 6 same-size squares. What mistake did Tess make?

_____

_____

Name _____

Partition Rectangles into Rows and Columns

Which rectangle has more same-size squares?

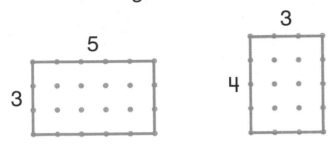

Draw lines to show same-size squares.
Then add the squares by row or by column.

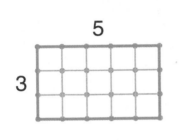

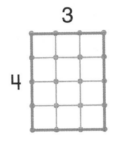

$5 + 5 + 5 = 15$
$3 + 3 + 3 + 3 + 3 = 15$

There are 15 squares in all.

$3 + 3 + 3 + 3 = 12$
$4 + 4 + 4 = 12$

There are 12 squares in all.

The blue rectangle has more same-size squares.

MORE PRACTICE

**Draw lines to show same-size squares.
Then write the total number of squares.**

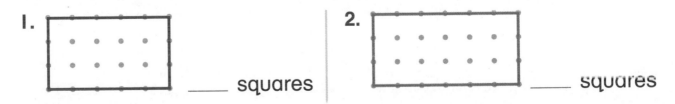

1. _____ squares

2. _____ squares

Draw lines in each rectangle to show same-size squares. Then match the rectangle with the total number of squares.

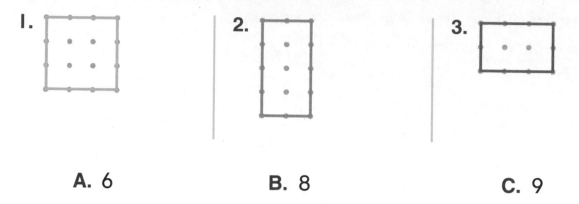

1.

2.

3.

A. 6

B. 8

C. 9

Problem Solving

4. Felix has 12 squares that are all the same size.
   He wants to use them to make a rectangle.
   What is one rectangle Felix can make?

   Felix can make a rectangle that has

   _____ rows with _____ squares in each row.

Write About It

5. One rectangle is made up of 2 columns of
   10 same-size squares. Another rectangle is
   made up of 5 columns of 4 same-size squares.
   Which rectangle is made up of more squares?
   Explain.

   _____

   _____

   _____

Halves

Zack has four sheets of construction paper.
He cuts each sheet into two pieces.
Which sheets of paper did Zack cut in half?

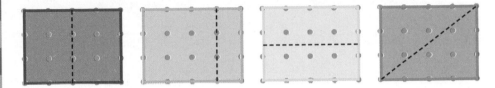

Objective
- Partition rectangles and circles into two equal shares.

Math Words
equal shares
half
two halves
whole

Equal shares are the same size. If there are two equal shares, each share is half of the rectangle.

The red rectangle is cut into two halves.
Two halves make one whole.

These pieces are the same size.
There are 2 equal shares.

These pieces are not the same size.

The green rectangle is not cut into equal shares. It is not cut into halves.

The yellow rectangle is cut into 2 equal shares.

The blue rectangle is cut into 2 equal shares.

> Zack cut the red, yellow, and blue sheets of paper in half.

Circle *halves* or *not halves* to describe each shape.

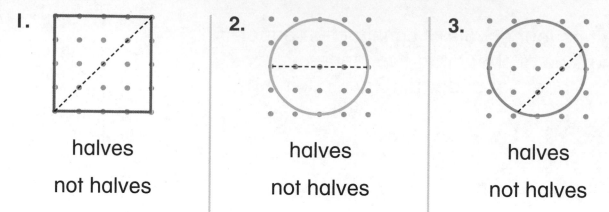

1.

halves

not halves

2.

halves

not halves

3.

halves

not halves

Draw two ways to split the rectangle in half.

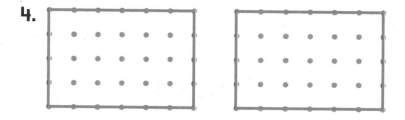

4.

Problem Solving

5. Ruby splits a rectangle in half. Each half is made up of 15 equal-size squares. How many squares make up the whole rectangle?

_____ squares

Write About It

6. Luis says the rectangle does not show halves because the parts are not the same shape. Is Luis correct? Explain.

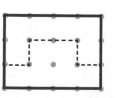

_____

_____

Name _____

Halves

Which rectangles show halves?

The parts are the same size.
There are 2 equal shares in the whole.
This rectangle shows halves.

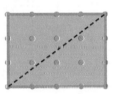

The parts are not the same size.

This rectangle does not show halves.

There are 2 equal shares.

There are 2 equal shares.

➤ The red, yellow, and blue rectangles show halves.

MORE PRACTICE

Circle *halves* or *not halves* to describe each shape.

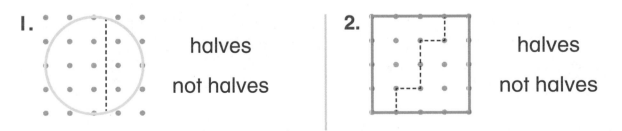

1. halves

    not halves

2. halves

    not halves

Draw four different ways to split the rectangle into halves.

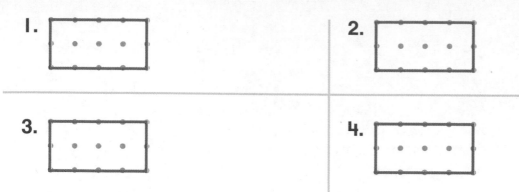

1.

2.

3.

4.

Problem Solving

5. Jeremiah draws a rectangle that is made up of 6 rows of 3 equal-size squares. Then he splits the rectangle into two halves. How many squares make up each half of the rectangle?

   Each half is made up of _____ squares.

Write About It

6. Taylor says the rectangle is split into halves because there are two parts. Is Taylor correct? Explain.

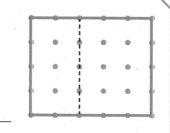

_____

_____

_____

_____

_____

Name _____

Draw lines to show same-size squares.
Then write the total number of squares.

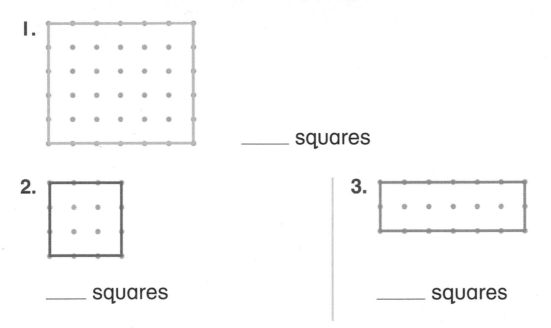

I.

_____ squares

2.

_____ squares

3.

_____ squares

Decide if each shape shows halves.
Circle *halves* or *not halves*.

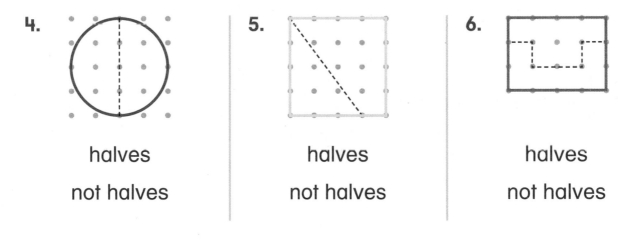

4.

halves

not halves

5.

halves

not halves

6.

halves

not halves

Draw two different ways to split each shape into halves.

7.

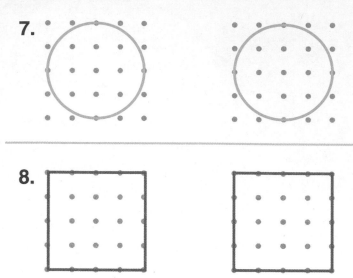

8.

Solve.

9. Valerie draws a rectangle that is made up of
   10 rows of 6 same-size squares. Then she splits
   the rectangle into two halves. How many squares
   make up each half of the rectangle?

   Each half is made up of ____ squares.

10. A rectangle made up of equal-size squares is cut
    into two pieces. One piece has 2 rows of 6 squares.
    The other piece has 3 rows of 4 squares.
    Is the rectangle cut into halves?
    Explain your reasoning.

    _____

    _____

    _____

    _____

Thirds

Jennifer says the red rectangle shows thirds. She says the orange rectangle does not show thirds because the parts are different shapes.

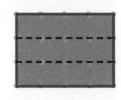

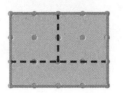

Objective
- Partition rectangles and circles into three equal shares.

Math Words
thirds
three thirds
whole

Is Jennifer correct?

If there are 3 equal shares, then a shape shows thirds.

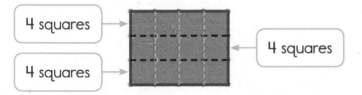

The parts are the same size.
There are 3 equal shares.

The red rectangle is split into three thirds.
Three thirds make one whole.

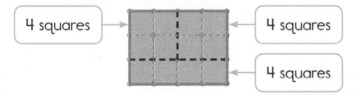

The parts are not the same shape, but they are the same size. There are 3 equal shares.

The orange rectangle is split into three thirds.

Jennifer is not correct. Both rectangles show thirds.

Circles can also be split into 3 equal shares.

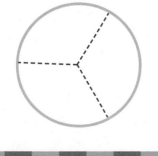

This circle shows thirds.

Decide if the shape shows thirds.
Circle *thirds* or *not thirds*.

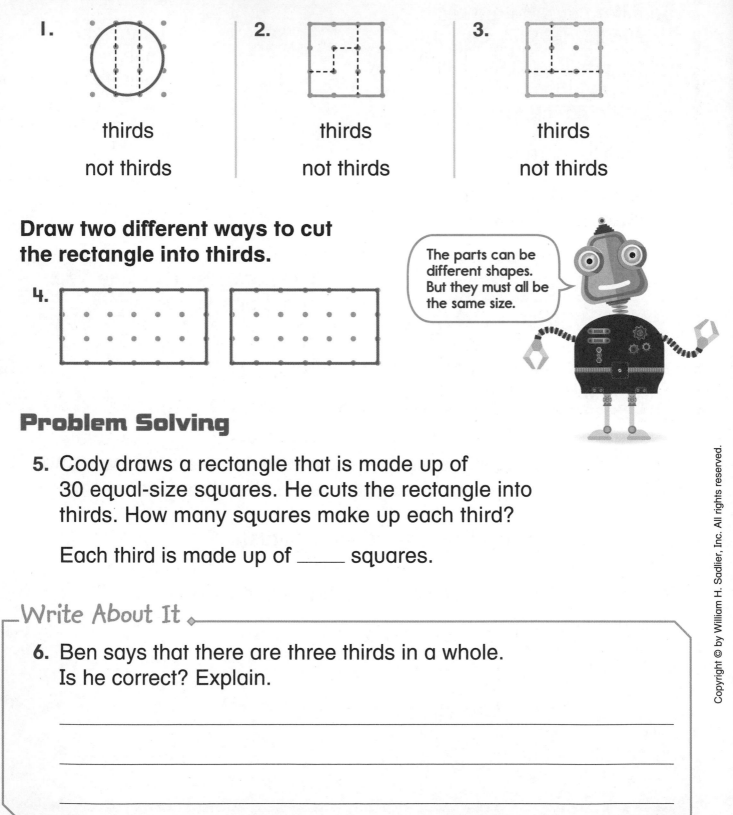

1.

thirds

not thirds

2.

thirds

not thirds

3.

thirds

not thirds

Draw two different ways to cut
the rectangle into thirds.

The parts can be
different shapes.
But they must all be
the same size.

4.

Problem Solving

5. Cody draws a rectangle that is made up of
30 equal-size squares. He cuts the rectangle into
thirds. How many squares make up each third?

Each third is made up of _____ squares.

Write About It

6. Ben says that there are three thirds in a whole.
Is he correct? Explain.

_____

_____

_____

Thirds

Which rectangle shows thirds?

If there are 3 equal shares, then a shape shows thirds.

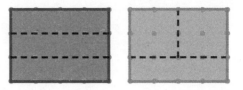

The parts are the same size. There are 3 equal shares.

The red rectangle shows thirds.

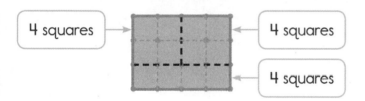

The parts are the same size. There are 3 equal shares.

The orange rectangle shows thirds.

▷ Both rectangles show thirds.

MORE PRACTICE

**Decide if each shape shows thirds.
Circle *thirds* or *not thirds*.**

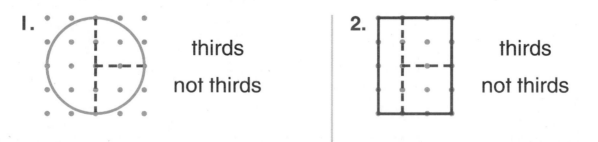

1.   thirds

                   not thirds

2.   thirds

                  not thirds

Draw three different ways to cut the square into thirds.

1.

2.

3.

Problem Solving

4. Margie draws a rectangle and cuts it into thirds. Each part is made up of 8 equal-size squares. How many squares make up the whole rectangle?

   The whole rectangle has _____ squares.

5. Elias draws a rectangle that is made up of 10 rows of 6 equal-size squares. Then he cuts the rectangle into thirds. How many squares make up each third?

   Each third is made up of _____ squares.

_Write About It

6. Sam says the rectangle shows thirds because the parts are the same size. Kay says it does not show thirds because the parts are different shapes. Who is correct? Explain.

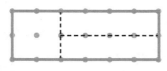

_____

_____

_____

Name _____

Fourths

Ian makes a pan of lasagna for 4 family members. Which ways can he cut the lasagna so that everyone gets an equal share?

Objective
▪ Partition rectangles and circles into four equal shares.

Math Words
fourths
four fourths
whole

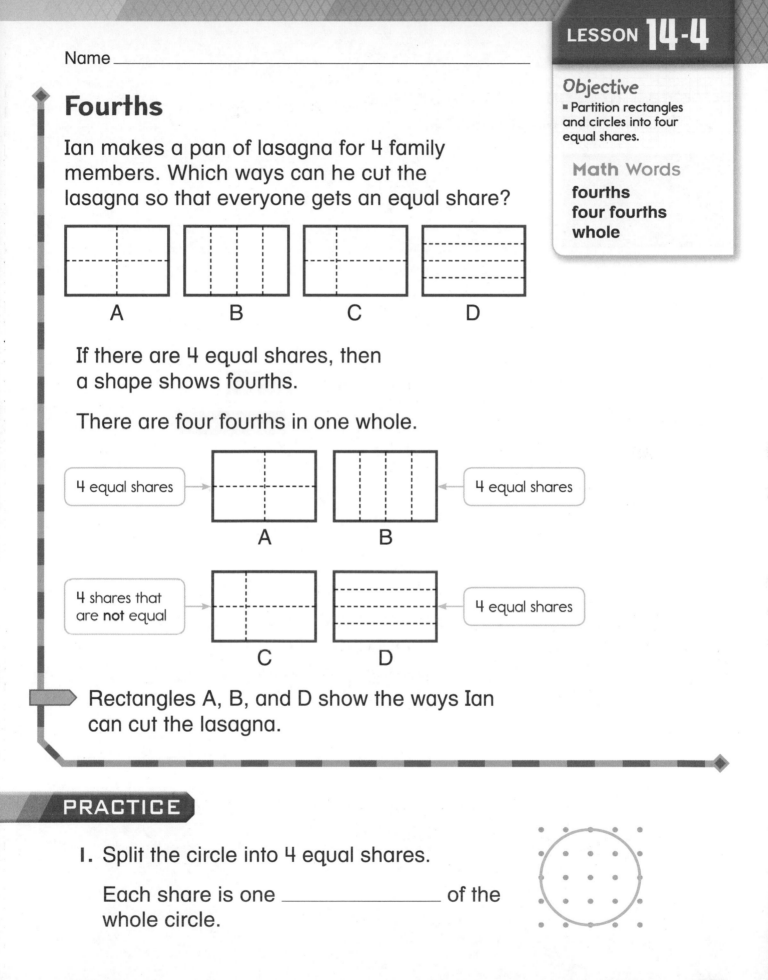

A   B   C   D

If there are 4 equal shares, then a shape shows fourths.

There are four fourths in one whole.

4 equal shares   A   B   4 equal shares

4 shares that are **not** equal   C   D   4 equal shares

▷ Rectangles A, B, and D show the ways Ian can cut the lasagna.

PRACTICE

I. Split the circle into 4 equal shares.

Each share is one _____ of the whole circle.

Decide if the shape shows fourths.
Circle *fourths* or *not fourths*.

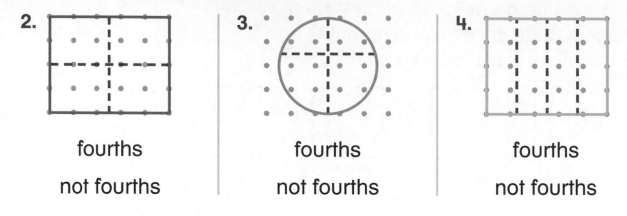

2.   fourths

   not fourths

3.   fourths

   not fourths

4.   fourths

   not fourths

Draw two different ways to show fourths.

5.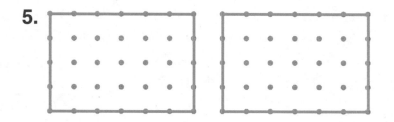

Problem Solving

6. Garrett draws a rectangle on dot paper and splits it into fourths. Each share is made up of 5 equal-size squares. How many squares make up the whole?

   The whole rectangle has _____ squares.

Write About It

7. How are halves, thirds, and fourths the same? How are they different?

_____

_____

Fourths

Name _____

Which rectangles show fourths?

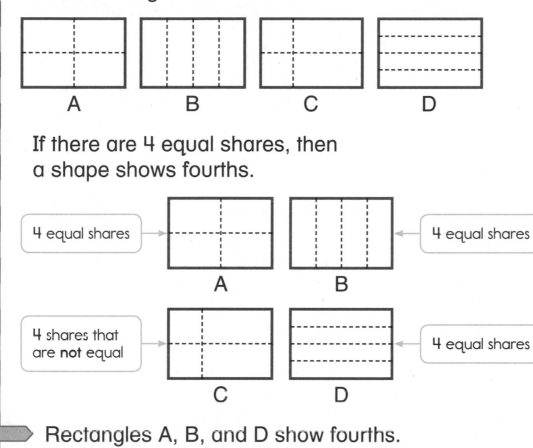

A   B   C   D

If there are 4 equal shares, then
a shape shows fourths.

4 equal shares → A   B ← 4 equal shares

4 shares that are **not** equal → C   D ← 4 equal shares

▷ Rectangles A, B, and D show fourths.

MORE PRACTICE

**Decide if each shape shows fourths.
Circle *fourths* or *not fourths*.**

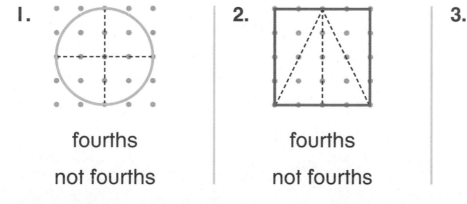

1.   fourths

    not fourths

2.   fourths

    not fourths

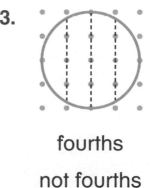

3.   fourths

    not fourths

Draw three different ways to split the rectangle into fourths.

1.

2.

3.

Problem Solving

4. Jordyn draws a rectangle that is made up of 8 equal-size squares. Then she splits the rectangle into fourths. How many squares make up each fourth of the rectangle?

   Each fourth is made up of _____ squares.

5. Lucas draws a rectangle that is made up of 8 rows of 5 equal-size squares. Then he splits the rectangle into fourths. How many squares make up each fourth of the rectangle?

   Each fourth is made up of _____ squares.

Write About It

6. Caroline says that any shape that is cut into 4 parts is cut into fourths. Is she correct? Explain.

   _____

   _____

   _____

LESSON 14-4

Name _____

Problem Solving Read 〉 Plan 〉 Solve 〉 Check
Use a Model

Jorge, Blake, and Derek volunteer to rake a field. They each make a plan for how to share the work equally. Which plan should the boys use?

Jorge's Plan   Blake's Plan   Derek's Plan

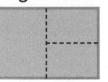 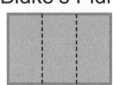 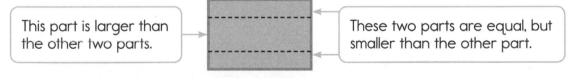

You can compare models to decide which plan to use.

Jorge's Plan

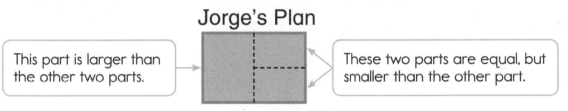

| This part is larger than the other two parts. | | These two parts are equal, but smaller than the other part. |

Jorge's plan does not share the work equally.

Blake's Plan

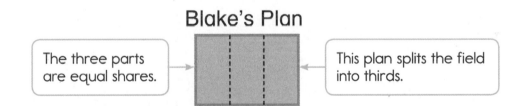

| The three parts are equal shares. | | This plan splits the field into thirds. |

Blake's plan shares the work equally.

Derek's Plan

| This part is larger than the other two parts. | | These two parts are equal, but smaller than the other part. |

Derek's plan does not share the work equally.

▷ Only Blake's plan has each boy raking an equal share of the field. The boys should use Blake's plan.

Read and solve each problem. You can compare models to help solve some of the problems.

1. Gabby and Ling make a large sandwich together. They each want to eat half. Circle the model that shows how the girls should cut the sandwich.

2. Arie makes two trays of muffins. The tray of pumpkin muffins has 5 rows with 6 in each row. The tray of banana muffins has 7 rows with 4 in each row. Arie made more of which type of muffin?

   Arie made more _____ muffins.

3. Darcy is thinking of one of these shapes. She says her shape has two fewer sides than a hexagon and is split into thirds. Circle Darcy's shape.

Write About It

4. Explain the strategy you used to find Darcy's shape.

   _____

   _____

   _____

Name_____

Problem Solving
Use a Model

Jorge, Blake, and Derek volunteer to rake a field. They each make a plan for how to share the work equally. Which plan should the boys use?

Jorge's Plan   Blake's Plan   Derek's Plan

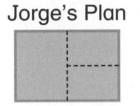 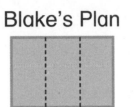 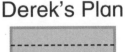

You can compare models to decide which plan to use.

Jorge's Plan

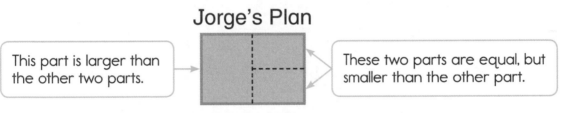

This part is larger than the other two parts. → These two parts are equal, but smaller than the other part.

Jorge's plan does not share the work equally.

Blake's Plan

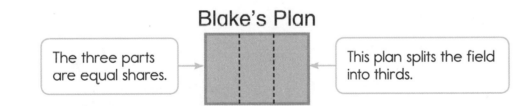

The three parts are equal shares. → This plan splits the field into thirds.

Blake's plan shares the work equally.

Derek's Plan

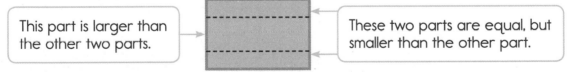

This part is larger than the other two parts. → These two parts are equal, but smaller than the other part.

Derek's plan does not share the work equally.

> Only Blake's plan has each boy raking an equal share of the field. The boys should use Blake's plan.

Read and solve each problem.

1. Caden, Bryson, Damian, and Charlie are brothers. Bryson is older than Charlie, but younger than Damian. Caden is not the oldest, but he is older than Bryson. What is the order of the brothers from youngest to oldest?

_____

2. Mariah has a piece of foam board that she will use to make signs. She wants to cut the board into fourths. Circle the model that shows how Mariah could cut the board.

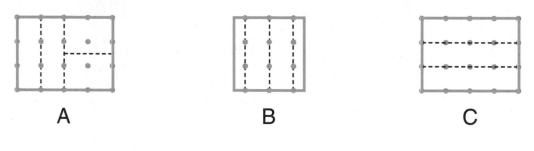

A   B   C

Write About It

3. Explain how you chose the model Mariah could use.

_____

_____

_____

_____

_____

_____

HOMEWORK

Read and solve each problem.

1. Julian makes a pizza for himself and 3 friends.
They want to share the pizza equally. Circle the
model that shows how Julian should cut the pizza.
Use the models to help you solve.

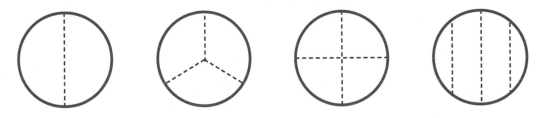

2. A farmer has a chicken coop with 4 rows of 7 nests.
There is 1 chicken in each nest. How many chickens
are in the coop?

   There are _____ chickens in the coop.

   If each chicken lays one egg per day, how many eggs
   do the chickens lay in all on Saturday and Sunday?

   The chickens lay _____ eggs in all.

3. Miranda describes a shape to her friend. She says
the shape has two more sides than a triangle and
is split into halves. Circle Miranda's shape.
Use the models to help you solve.

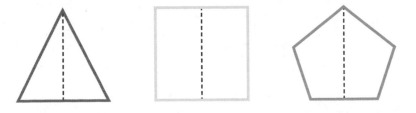

Read and solve each problem.

4. Rana has a rectangular garden. She wants to plant a fourth of the garden with tomatoes, a fourth with carrots, a fourth with cucumbers, and a fourth with peppers. Which plan or plans could Rana use for her garden?

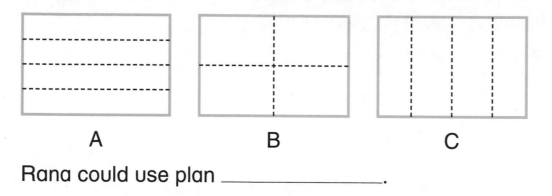

   A   B   C

   Rana could use plan _____.

5. Jacob thinks of a three-digit mystery number. He says the hundreds digit is 6 more than the ones digit. He says the number has 4 tens. What could be Jacob's number?

   Jacob's number could be _____, _____, or _____.

Write About It

6. Explain the strategy you used to find all the possibilities for Jacob's mystery number.

   _____

   _____

   _____

   _____

Name _____

Use the dots to split each rectangle into same-size squares. Then write the total number of squares.

1.

_____ squares

2.

_____ squares

Draw two different ways to split the rectangle into halves.

3.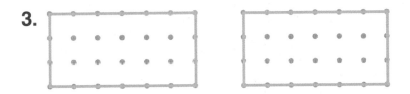

Draw two different ways to split the rectangle into thirds.

4.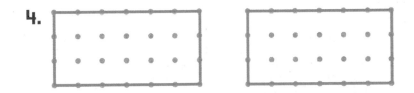

Draw two different ways to split the rectangle into fourths.

5.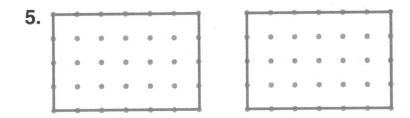

Draw each rectangle.

6. a rectangle made up of
20 squares, split into halves

. . . .
. . . .
. . . .
. . . .
. . . .
. . . .
. . . .

7. a rectangle made up of
12 squares, split into thirds

. . . .
. . . .
. . . .
. . . .
. . . .
. . . .
. . . .

Solve.

8. A red rectangle is split into fourths. Each fourth
is made up of 3 rows of 2 equal-size squares.
A blue rectangle is the same size as the red rectangle,
but it is split into thirds. How many squares make up
each third of the blue rectangle?

Each third is made up of _____ squares.

9. Omar is painting a picture in art class.
He plans to paint his canvas in fourths.
Which plan should Omar use?

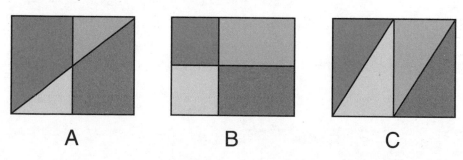

A   B   C

Omar should use Plan _____ for his painting.

A farmer has a large field that is separated into equal-size square plots. There are 12 rows of plots with 10 plots in each row.

1. How many plots are in the whole field? Explain.

   _____

   _____

   _____

   _____

2. The farmer plans to water half the field one week and half the field the next week. How many plots will she water each week?

   The farmer will water _____ plots each week.

   How can the farmer split the field into 2 equal shares? How many rows and columns are in each half? More than one answer is correct.

   _____ rows and _____ columns

3. Draw a model on grid paper of the farmer's field.

   • Choose a way to split the field into fourths. Write how many plots are in each section.

   • Research to find out which plants might grow best in your area. How much sun and rainfall do the plants need?

   • Decide which crops to plant in each section of the field. Label your model and share it with the class.

Determine the best answer for each problem.

1. Subtract.

   84 − 39 = _____

2. Add.

   17 + 54 + 23 = _____

3. Use mental math to compare.

   72 − 15 (?) 19 + 38

   A. <
   B. >
   C. =

4. Use mental math to compare.

   34 + 29 (?) 100 − 35

   A. <
   B. >
   C. =

5. Which has a difference greater than 80?

   A. 173 − 92
   B. 168 − 89
   C. 141 − 61

6. Which has a sum greater than 200?

   A. 122 + 78
   B. 107 + 92
   C. 86 + 117

7. What would be the total number of squares in the array?

   7 rows of 4 squares

   _____ squares

8. What would be the total number of squares in the array?

   9 rows of 10 squares

   _____ squares

9. Find the unknown value.

   412 + _____ = 801

10. Find the unknown value.

    672 − _____ = 615

A

A.M. Letters that show a time at or after midnight and before noon.

add To find how many in all.

$$3 + 2 = 5$$

addend A number that is added to another number or numbers.

$$6 + 4 = 10$$
addend   addend

addition equation An addition number sentence with an equal sign.

addition fact An equation of the form part + part = whole.

angle of a polygon The space between two sides of a polygon that meet.

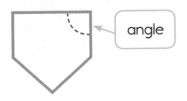
angle

array A set of objects arranged in rows and columns.

Associative Property of Addition Changing the grouping of the addends does not change the sum.
Example:
$$(2 + 6) + 4 = 2 + (6 + 4)$$

B

bar graph A graph that uses bars to show data. The bars may be of different lengths.

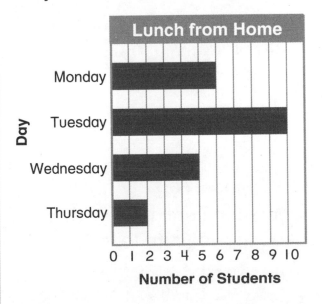

Lunch from Home

Day

Monday
Tuesday
Wednesday
Thursday

0 1 2 3 4 5 6 7 8 9 10
Number of Students

bar model A diagram that uses a series of rectangles to represent the parts and the whole of a problem.

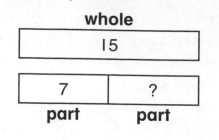

break apart To write a number as the sum of lesser numbers.

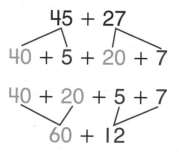

centimeter (cm) A unit of metric measure to describe length.

This is 1 centimeter: ⊢—⊣.

centimeter ruler A tool, labeled in centimeters, that is used to measure length.

change Money received back when an amount paid is greater than the total amount due.

column A vertical arrangement of objects or numbers.

compare To describe a number as greater than (>), less than (<), or equal to (=) another number.
Example: 153 > 145

cone A solid shape with one curved surface and one flat surface shaped like a circle.

corner The point at which sides of a two-dimensional shape or edges of a three-dimensional shape meet.

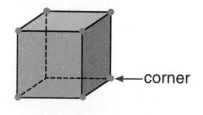

corner

count backwards (count back) To name numbers in decreasing order.

counting on To start at a given number and count forward from that number.

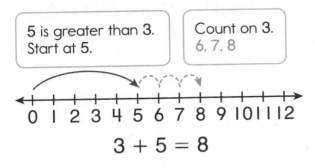

| 5 is greater than 3. Start at 5. | Count on 3. 6, 7, 8 |

$$3 + 5 = 8$$

cube A solid shape with 6 flat surfaces all shaped like squares.

customary unit A unit in the customary system of measurement.
Examples: inch, foot, and yard

cylinder A solid shape with one curved surface and two flat surfaces shaped like circles.

data A set of collected values or information.

diagonal In a table or array, from the bottom left to the top right or from the top left to the bottom right.

diagram A visual model of a problem or solution.

difference The result of subtracting.

digit 0, 1, 2, 3, 4, 5, 6, 7, 8, or 9.

dime A coin that is worth 10 cents.

dollar sign The symbol $.

doubles – I strategy To find a sum where one addend is I more than the other addend, use the doubles fact for the greater addend and subtract I.

Example: since 4 + 4 = 8
then 4 + 3 = 7

doubles + I strategy To find a sum where one addend is I more than the other addend, use the doubles fact for the lesser addend and add I.

Example: since 7 + 7 = 14
then 7 + 8 = 15

doubles fact A two-addend addition equation in which both addends are the same.

Example: 9 + 9 = 18

E

edge The line segment where two faces of a three-dimensional figure meet.

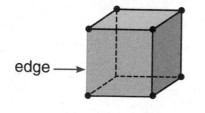

edge →

equal addends Addends that are the same; the sum of two equal addends is always an even number.

equal amounts of money Groups of money that total the same amount even if they are made up of different coins and bills.

equal shares Pieces of one whole that are the same size.

Example:

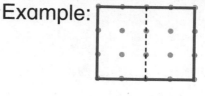

equal sign The symbol =.

equal to (=) To have the same value as.

equals = A symbol that means to have the same value as.

Example: 35 = 35

equation A number sentence with an equal sign (=) that shows the value on the left side is the same as the value on the right side.

Example: 15 + 10 = 25

estimate An approximate answer; to find an answer that is close to the exact answer.

even number A number with none left over if you count by 2s or make pairs. Even numbers have 0, 2, 4, 6, or 8 in the ones place.

expanded form A form that shows a number written as the sum of the place values of each digit.

Example: The expanded form of 173 is 100 + 70 + 3.

F

face A flat surface with straight sides on a three-dimensional figure.

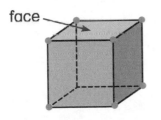

face

fact family A set of related facts for a given group of numbers.

Example:
$$4 + 7 = 11$$
$$11 - 7 = 4$$
$$7 + 4 = 11$$
$$11 - 4 = 7$$

fifty-dollar bill A piece of paper money worth fifty dollars, or $50.

five-dollar bill A piece of paper money worth five dollars, or $5.

foot (ft) A customary unit of measure to describe length that equals 12 inches.

four fourths All parts of a whole that is divided into 4 equal parts.

fourth One part of a whole that is divided into 4 equal parts.

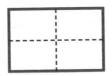

Each equal share is one fourth.

G

greater than (>) A symbol showing that one number has a greater value than another number.
Example: 27 > 19

greatest Having the largest value.

group To put together.

H

half One part of a whole that is divided into 2 equal parts.

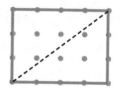

Each equal share is one half.

half hour A measure of time equal to 30 minutes.

half past Describes one half hour or 30 minutes past an hour.

hexagon A flat shape with 6 sides and 6 corners.

hour A unit of time that equals 60 minutes.

hour hand The short hand on an analog clock that shows the hour.

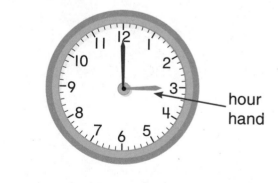

hour hand

hundred I hundred = 10 tens = 100 ones.

hundred flat A square divided into 100 equal parts.

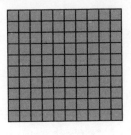

I

inch (in.) A customary unit of measure to describe length. This is 1 inch: ⊢————⊣.

inch ruler A tool used to measure length in inches.

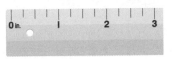

K

key A statement showing how many data items each symbol stands for in a picture graph.

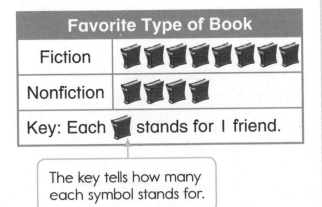

The key tells how many each symbol stands for.

L

least Having the smallest value.

length Measurement along a straight line from end to end.

less than (<) A symbol showing that one number has a lesser value than another number.
Example: 32 < 47

line plot A graph that uses X marks on a number line to represent data.

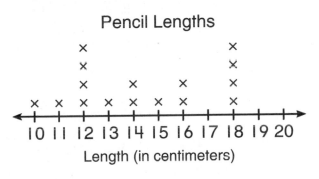

logical reasoning Using correct thought processes and steps to solve a problem.

M

make 10 A strategy for adding or subtracting in which numbers in the problem are broken apart to form sums or differences equal to 10.

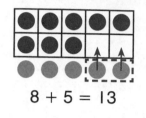

$8 + 5 = 13$

measure To describe an object with a number by using a tool such as a ruler.

measuring tape A long, flexible strip of plastic or metal that is marked at intervals for measuring length.

meter (m) A metric unit of measure that is equal to 100 centimeters.

meterstick A ruler used to measure length in centimeters and meters.

metric unit A unit in the metric system of measurement. Examples: centimeters and meters

minus sign (−) A symbol that means to subtract or take away.

minute A unit of time that equals 60 seconds.

minute hand The long hand on an analog clock that shows the minute.

minute hand

model A diagram or picture that represents a problem or helps to solve a problem.

$6 \quad + \quad 4 \quad = \quad 10$

N

near doubles fact A two-addend addition equation in which one addend is 1 more or 1 less than the other.

nickel A coin worth 5 cents.

number line A line that shows numbers in order using a scale.

number name The word form for a number.
Example: 96 is ninety-six

O

odd number A number with one left over if you count by 2s or make pairs. Odd numbers have 1, 3, 5, 7, or 9 in the ones place.

one-dollar bill A piece of paper money worth one dollar, or $1.

one hundred-dollar bill A piece of paper money worth one hundred dollars, or $100.

one less A number less than another number by 1.

one more A number greater than another number by 1.

ones 10 ones = 1 ten

P

P.M. Letters that show a time at or after noon and before midnight.

pattern An arrangement of objects or values that follows a rule.

pattern rule A rule that tells what order objects appear in a pattern.

penny A coin worth 1 cent.

pentagon A polygon with 5 sides and 5 angles.

picture graph A graph that uses pictures to represent numbers of real-world objects.

Favorite Season	
Fall	🍁🍁🍁🍁
Winter	🍁🍁🍁🍁🍁
Spring	🍁🍁🍁
Summer	🍁🍁🍁🍁🍁🍁🍁
Key: Each 🍁 stands for 1 student.	

place value The value of a digit depending on its position, or place, in a number.

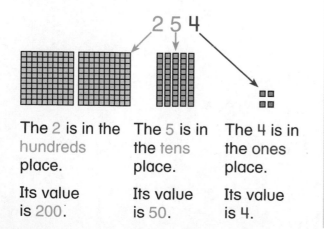

The 2 is in the hundreds place.

Its value is 200.

The 5 is in the tens place.

Its value is 50.

The 4 is in the ones place.

Its value is 4.

place-value chart A chart that shows the value of each digit in a number.

hundreds	tens	ones
2	5	4

plus sign (+) A symbol that means to add.

polygon A closed plane figure made up of line segments that meet at vertices but do not cross.

pyramid A solid figure whose base is a polygon and whose faces are triangles with a common vertex.

Q

quadrilateral A polygon with 4 sides and 4 angles.

Examples: rectangle, square, trapezoid

quarter A coin worth 25 cents.

R

rectangle A shape with 4 sides and 4 corners.

rectangular prism A solid figure with 6 rectangular faces.

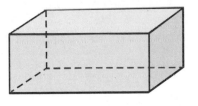

regroup To rename ten in a place as one in the next greater place, or one in a place as ten in the next lesser place, in order to add or subtract.

related addition facts Addition facts that use the same numbers.

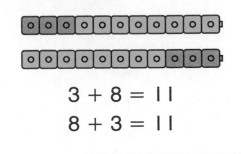

$$3 + 8 = 11$$
$$8 + 3 = 11$$

related subtraction facts Subtraction facts that use the same numbers.

$$12 - 3 = 9$$
$$12 - 9 = 3$$

row A horizontal arrangement of objects or numbers.

ruler A tool used to measure length, usually labeled in inches along one edge and centimeters on the opposite edge.

S

side A line segment that forms part of a shape.

skip count To count by a number that is not 1. Example: Skip count from 0 by 2s: 2, 4, 6, 8, 10

sphere A round three-dimensional figure.

square A shape with 4 sides of equal length and 4 corners.

standard form of a number The numeral form of a number.

subtract To take away; to find how many are left.

$$6 - 2 = 4$$

subtraction equation A subtraction number sentence with an equal sign. Example: $9 - 6 = 3$

sum The result of adding.

$$6 \quad + \quad 4 \quad = \quad 10$$

sum

symbol A picture or character that stands for something. Key: Each stands for 1 student. ← symbol

T

table An organized chart of rows and columns.

Fruit	Number Sold
Peaches	133
Apples	167
Bananas	138
Mangoes	159

take apart To separate a group into two or more smaller groups.

$$10 - 3 = 7$$

tally chart A chart that organizes data and uses tally marks to record frequency.

Jump Distances	
Distance (in feet)	Tally
3	II
4	IIII II
5	IIII
6	I

tally mark A mark used in a tally chart to help record frequency of data.

ten-dollar bill A piece of paper money worth ten dollars, or $10.

ten-frame A rectangular chart with 2 rows and 5 columns that is used to represent numbers less than or equal to 10.

tens number A number with tens and no ones.

third One part of a whole that is divided into 3 equal parts.

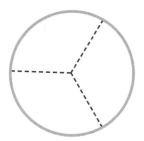

Each equal share is one third.

three thirds All parts of a whole that is divided into 3 equal parts.

three-digit number A number consisting of hundreds, tens, and ones.

hundreds	tens	ones
5	6	4

five hundred sixty-four 564

three-dimensional shape A solid figure that has measurements of length, width, and height.

triangle A shape with 3 sides and 3 corners.

twenty-dollar bill A piece of paper money worth twenty dollars, or $20.

two-dimensional shape A shape with length and width, but no thickness.

two halves All parts of a whole that is divided into 2 equal parts.

U

unknown A missing value or part.

unknown addend An addend whose value is not known and is usually represented by a box or a question mark.

V

vertex (vertices) The point where three edges of a solid figure meet.

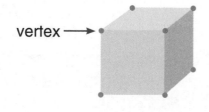

vertex →

W

whole All of something.

whole number Any of the numbers 0, 1, 2, 3, 4, ...

work backward A strategy where the answer is known and the unknown is found by reversing the operations or steps in the problem.

Y

yard (yd) A customary unit of measure to describe length that equals 3 feet.

yardstick A ruler used to measure length in feet and yards.

Centimeter Grid Paper

Dot Paper

Money

Attribute Blocks